Human and Social Biology Examination Questions and Objective Test Items

L. Fairclough, B.Sc., M.I.Biol.

Senior Biologist, Deane High School, Bolton.

HODDER AND STOUGHTON
LONDON   SYDNEY   AUCKLAND   TORONTO

Acknowledgements

I would like to record my gratitude to all those who gave help and encouragement during the writing of this book. Dr. H. Vickers, St. Martin's College of Education and Mr. J. Green, St. Mary's High School made numerous helpful suggestions during the early stages of preparation. Special thanks are due to Mr. R. E. Lister, formerly Head of the Department of Biological Science, University of London Institute of Education and former Chief Examiner for Nuffield Advanced Level Biology, for reading the entire manuscript and for his constructive criticisms and suggestions for improvement, most of which I have been glad to carry out.

I am indebted to my present and former students for their invaluable co-operation in pretesting the questions and to Mrs. C. I. Pilkington and Mrs. C. Wright for their patience in the preparation of the typescript.

In conclusion, I would like to acknowledge the assistance I have received from Mrs. Beryl Gell and Mr. Jonathan Wray of Hodder and Stoughton Educational.

L. Fairclough
1979

For Kirsty and Emma

British Library Cataloguing in Publication Data

Fairclough, L
   Human and social biology.
   1. Human physiology – Examinations, questions, etc.
   1. Title
   612'.0076   QP36

   ISBN 0–340–25025–9 Complete Volume
   ISBN 0–340–24339–2 Test Volume

First Printed 1980

Printed in Great Britain for Hodder and Stoughton Educational, a division of Hodder and Stoughton Ltd., Mill Road, Dunton Green, Sevenoaks, Kent, by Richard Clay (The Chaucer Press) Ltd, Bungay, Suffolk

Phototypesetting by Rainbow Graphics, Liverpool

Contents

		Page
Acknowledgements		ii
Preface		iv
To the student		v
1	Cell, Tissues, Organs and the Structure of the Body	1
2	Food and Diet	10
3	Nutrition and Digestion	19
4	Respiration	29
5	Blood and Circulation	38
6	Excretion and the Skin	48
7	Skeleton, Muscles and Movement	57
8	Nervous and Hormonal Co-ordination	66
9	Growth and Reproduction	75
10	Inheritance and Population	87
11	Microbiology and Disease	99
12	Social Hygiene	112

Preface

The purpose of this book is to provide a source of questions with which teachers and students can accurately assess progress in Human Biology at CSE and GCE 'O', level. The questions also provide a means by which gaps in knowledge and understanding or particular weaknesses can be quickly pinpointed before a final examination.

The questions can, of course, be used in a variety of ways, but they have been written with three basic aims in mind: to provide a source of questions for homework purposes, as a means of assessing the progress of students throughout a course and for revision and practice in the final stages of preparation before an examination. Students will derive most benefit from the questions if opportunities for discussion and reflection are provided. Used in this way the biological information within the questions will itself serve as a useful teaching aid.

The emphasis in the present-day examination system has moved away from testing straightforward factual knowledge. As well as testing the candidate's memory, examinations are now designed to assess other aspects of his ability, such as the understanding and interpretation of the subject matter. The questions included here reflect this change in emphasis and have been selected to test the following abilities: the knowledge and understanding of biological facts and principles, the application of that knowledge and the ability to evaluate, analyse and interpret biological information.

An important consideration in the choice of questions has been that they should not be merely a vehicle for restating facts, although factual knowledge remains important, but that they should also improve the student's understanding of the subject matter. To this end, some use has been made in the objective questions of the negative answer. In this type of question the student is required to pick out from the options provided the one which is false. This has the advantage of avoiding presenting the reader with too much incorrect information, some of which may be absorbed, and it is also useful in that it necessitates careful consideration of each alternative response.

The majority of questions are objective items, but to these have been added a considerable number of structured questions, which now form the basis of many examinations. The objective items are of four types — multiple choice, multiple completion, matching pairs and assertion/reason. Many CSE and GCE Examination Boards have now introduced such questions as an integral part of their examinations and, although these are difficult to prepare, they provide the most precise and versatile method of evaluating progress. Such questions have the added advantage of quick and easy marking. (Teachers wishing to prepare their own objective questions are recommended to refer to the following publication – *'Objective Testing. A guide for Science Teachers.'* by E. W. Jenkins, published by the Centre for Studies in Science Education, The University, Leeds.) The structured items have been designed to provide students with a selection of questions of varying difficulty level of the type likely to be encountered in a final examination.

Within each chapter the questions have been grouped under basic concept areas and the items are therefore arranged in a specific order. It is hoped that this arrangement of material will facilitate the selection of items from the various concept areas for the purpose of constructing tests and at the same time give adequate test experience of basic principles and of the various question types.

The questions have been compiled to cover the majority of examination syllabuses in Human Biology at CSE and GCE 'O' level and have been thoroughly pre-tested with candidates following these courses. In addition they will prove useful for students following a Pre-Nursing or Preliminary Nursing course as well as students in Further Education engaged in courses such as Human Physiology and Hygiene.

L. Fairclough
February, 1979

To the student

The following advice is given in order that you may use the knowledge you possess to the best possible advantage. Although much of it may appear to be simply common sense, it remains a fact that many examination candidates continue to lose marks needlessly because they do not follow certain basic rules. Perhaps the most common errors that occur are caused by failure to read questions properly, failure to obey specific instructions and by writing irrelevant material. Following the advice given below will help you to develop a good examination technique.

1   Read the instructions *carefully* and obey any instructions given. If, for example, the instructions direct the candidate to answer four questions and five are answered then the last question will not be marked.

2   It is particularly important to consider carefully the wording of the question. If, for example, a question asks you to name the causative organism of malaria, an answer of the mosquito is clearly incorrect since this organism is the vector of the disease not its cause. The correct answer is, of course, *Plasmodium*.

3   It is often useful to prepare a rough plan or summary of your answer.

4   It is good practice to pause during the writing of an answer to check that you are actually answering the question on the paper and not writing irrelevant material that may be perfectly correct but which will not gain marks and will also waste valuable time. For example, consider the following question and answer. 'Give an account of the functions of the blood'. The candidate's answer included details of the structure of blood vessels, the mechanism of the heartbeat and details of ventilation of the lungs. Although this information was correct it was clearly not necessary in the answer to such a question. It therefore, gained no marks and also wasted time which could have been more gainfully employed. In many examination papers it is possible to estimate the length of the answer required by the amount of space allocated to the answer. If this is not the case use your common sense!

5   Give sufficient detail in your answers. For example, in a question such as the one above, you will certainly lose marks if you do not mention the role of haemoglobin.

6   If a question has several parts, answer these in the order in which they appear in the question.

7   Unless a paper contains compulsory questions, in which case the time allowed is often given, divide your time equally between the questions. It is also advisable to keep an eye on the clock. Do not spend a disproportionate amount of time on any one question. Aim to finish the paper with enough time to spare to allow you to read through your answers.

8   Avoid repetition of facts as this does not gain marks.

9   Diagrams should be large, clearly drawn and fully labelled. Shading and stippling should be avoided as this is not only time-consuming but also often confuses rather than clarifies the diagram. Similarly the use of colours is to be avoided. Guide lines should actually *touch* the structures to which they refer. Remember that a diagram should be used in place of the text or as a supplement to it. Do not duplicate material by giving a written description as well as a diagram but you must refer to the diagram in the written account. A diagram must serve a purpose and must not be used merely to decorate your answer. Diagrams used in an answer should be placed just before the relevant text. This makes the answer easier to read and to mark. On no account should diagrams be grouped together at the end of the answer.

10 Always be as precise and accurate as possible. For example, do not call a structure the windpipe if you know the term trachea.

11 In objective questions it is particularly important to read the instructions telling you how to answer the questions *carefully*. In this type of question the answer required is usually *one* only of the letters **A, B, C, D** or **E**. Do not give two answers to such questions.

12 Objective questions usually gain only 1 or 2 marks and you should not spend a large amount of time on any one question. Work through the paper quickly but thoroughly and leave any questions that you find too difficult until later. These can then be attempted on your second time through the paper.

13 It is advisable to avoid completely wild guesses in objective questions, but on the other hand if you have no idea at all, choose the most likely answer and write this down — blank spaces do not gain marks.

14 It is important that any mistakes or errors should be clearly crossed out.

15 Finally, always use any time left at the end of the examination to read through and check your answers. This can often gain valuable marks.

1. Cells, Tissues, Organs and the Structure of the Body

Multiple Choice

In each of the following questions choose *one* only of the letters **A, B, C, D** or **E** to indicate your answer.

1 Mature cells which do *not* contain a nucleus are

   A white blood cells
   B muscle cells
   C nerve cells
   D red blood cells
   E cells of the liver.

2 DNA is found

   A only in mitochondria
   B only in ribosomes
   C within the nucleus
   D outside the cell only
   E in the greatest quantity in the cytoplasm.

   Refer to Fig. 1 and then answer questions 3 and 4.

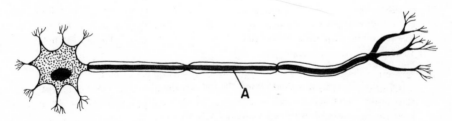

Fig. 1

3 The cell shown above would be found in the greatest numbers in

   A tooth enamel
   B the outermost layer of the skin
   C blood
   D the spinal cord
   E bone.

4 The part labelled A in the diagram above is the

   A sarcoplasm
   B axon
   C cell body
   D collagen
   E periosteum.

5   Which of the following is *not* true of a specialized cell?

   A It has developed one particular function.
   B Its shape has been adapted to its specialized function.
   C It can still carry out respiration.
   D It usually retains its ability to reproduce.
   E It is usually incapable of independent existence.

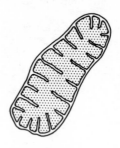

Fig. 2

Study Fig. 2 above and then answer questions 6 and 7.

6   The cell organelle shown in Fig. 2 is a

   A lysosome
   B nucleus
   C ribosome
   D mitochondrion
   E vacuole.

7   The function of the organelle shown in Fig. 2 is the

   A removal of carbon dioxide from the cytoplasm
   B production of lactic acid
   C removal of excess water from the cytoplasm
   D production of ATP
   E production of cell proteins.

8   Which of the following is a tissue?

   A skin
   B cardiac muscle
   C biceps
   D liver
   E stomach.

9   A tissue is

   A a group of similar cells
   B a group of cells with the same function
   C a group of different types of cells
   D a structure composed of at least 3 different cell types
   E the material from which cartilage is composed.

10 Which of the following is *not* an organ?

A heart
B stomach
C kidney
D skeleton
E liver.

Refer to Fig. 3 and then answer questions 11–13.

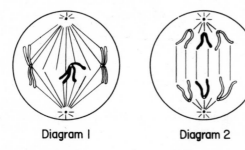

Diagram 1   Diagram 2

Fig. 3

11 The stage in mitosis represented by Diagram 1 is

A interphase
B anaphase
C metaphase
D prophase
E telophase.

12 The stage in mitosis represented by Diagram 2 is

A interphase
B anaphase
C metaphase
D prophase
E telophase.

13 The stage in mitosis which follows that shown in Diagram 2 is

A interphase
B anaphase
C metaphase
D prophase
E telophase.

14 When a cell divides by meiosis how many daughter cells are produced?

A the same number as in a normal mitotic division
B half as many as in a mitotic division
C 8
D millions
E twice as many as in a mitotic division.

3

15 The study of the functioning of the body is called

    A cytology
    B physiology
    C anatomy
    D histology
    E zoology.

16 The smallest bones in the body are found

    A supporting the pinna of the ear
    B in the trachea
    C in the ankle
    D in the wrist
    E in the middle ear.

Multiple Completion

For each of the following incomplete statements or questions *one* or *more* of the responses numbered 1–4 are correct.

Choose the appropriate letter as your answer according to the following code

    A — if only 1, 2 and 3 are correct
    B — if only 1, 2 and 4 are correct
    C — if only 1 and 4 are correct
    D — if only 3 is correct
    E — if only 2, 3 and 4 are correct.

17 Functions of adipose (fatty) tissue include

    1 insulation against heat loss
    2 storage of glycogen
    3 secretion of enzymes
    4 protection against physical injury.

18 Haversian canals are found in

    1 cartilage
    2 keratin
    3 bone
    4 connective tissue.

19 Which of the following is (are) organs?

    1 cartilage
    2 spinal cord
    3 salivary glands
    4 triceps.

20 Functions of the liver include

    1 storage of iron
    2 manufacture of plasma proteins
    3 storage of glycogen
    4 storage of vitamins C, B_1, B_{12} and K.

21 Which of the following organelles is (are) common to both plant and animal cells?

1 mitochondrion
2 nucleus
3 endoplasmic reticulum
4 cell wall.

22 Functions of the lymphatic system include

1 transport of fats
2 production of red blood cells
3 storage of vitamins in lymph nodes
4 destruction of bacteria.

Matching Pairs

Each set of questions consists of five lettered headings **A, B, C, D** and **E** followed by four numbered items. Answer each question by choosing the *one* heading (**A, B, C, D** or **E**) that is related most closely to the item concerned.

EACH HEADING MAY BE USED ONCE, MORE THAN ONCE OR NOT AT ALL.

Questions 23–26

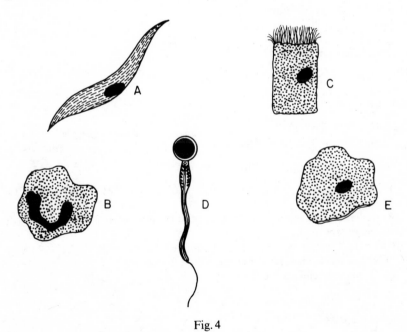

Fig. 4

Which of the cells represented in Fig. 4

23 has only 23 chromosomes?
24 lines the trachea?
25 is found in the blood?
26 can engulf bacteria?

Questions 27–30

Which of the following cell organelles

    A nucleus
    B ribosome
    C endoplasmic reticulum
    D mitochondrion
    E plasma membrane

27 can exclude substances from the cell?
28 is the site of protein synthesis?
29 is an internal system of membranes?
30 controls the activities of the cell?

Questions 31–34

    A oesophagus
    B diaphragm
    C kidney
    D pulmonary artery
    E carotid artery

Which of the above structures

31 is found only in the thoracic cavity?
32 passes through the diaphragm?
33 separates the abdominal and thoracic cavities?
34 is found only in the abdominal cavity?

Assertion/Reason

Each of the following questions consists of an *assertion* and a *reason*. Consider both statements and then choose the letter **A, B, C, D** or **E** as your answer according to the following

    A —if both statements are true, and the reason is a correct explanation of the assertion
    B —if both statements are true, but the reason is not a correct explanation of the assertion
    C —if the assertion is true, but the reason is false
    D —if the assertion is false, but the reason is true
    E —if both statements are false.

Code Summarized

	ASSERTION	REASON	
A	true	true	reason is a correct explanation
B	true	true	reason is not a correct explanation
C	true	false	
D	false	true	
E	false	false	

ASSERTION		REASON
35 All cells contain a nucleus	*because*	the nucleus controls the activities of the cell
36 Red cells are the most numerous in the blood	*because*	red cells transport carbon dioxide.
37 Red blood cells placed in a hypertonic solution will burst	*because*	red blood cells in an hypertonic solution gain water by osmosis
38 The pulp cavity of a tooth contains blood capillaries	*because*	the cells of the tooth require a supply of oxygen.
39 During metaphase the spindle fibres disappear	*because*	at metaphase the chromatids have moved to opposite poles of the cell.

Structured Questions

40 The diagram below represents the structure of a 'typical' cell as seen under the electron microscope.

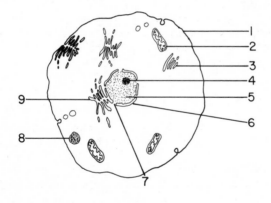

Fig. 5

a) Name the structures numbered 1–9 in Fig. 5.
b) Give one function of 1, 2 & 5.
c) Name the structures, not shown in the diagram, which are present in the part numbered 5.
d) When do these structures become visible?
e) Why is this cell described as a 'typical' cell?
f) For each of the following cells state two ways in which they would differ in structure from the cell shown above

   (i) red blood cell
   (ii) motor nerve cell
   (iii) muscle cell
   (iv) sperm cell.

41 The diagrams in Fig. 6 show 6 types of cell found in the human body.

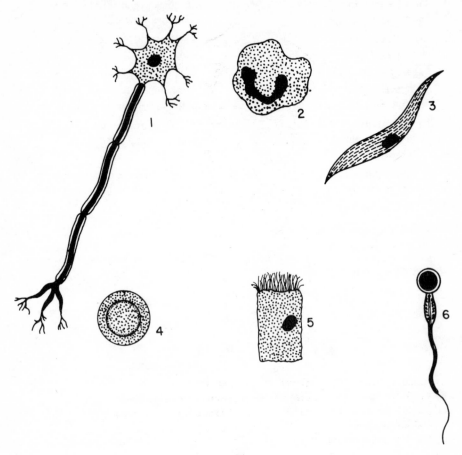

Fig. 6

a) Name each type of cell.
b) State one position in the body where each type of cell can be found.
c) Give one function for each type of cell.
d) State one specialised feature of each cell type shown.

42 Below is a list of secretions produced by the body. For each one state

(i) the structure which produces it
(ii) two substances present in the secretion
(iii) *one* function of the secretion.

    a) bile
    b) sweat
    c) saliva
    d) milk
    e) tear fluid
    f) urine
    g) gastric juice.

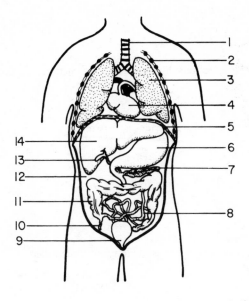

Fig. 7

a) Name the structures numbered 1–14 in Fig. 7.
b) Mark with an X on the diagram the position of the left kidney.
c) Name three structures, not shown on this diagram, which are found in the abdominal cavity.
d) Give the numbers *only* of those structures which have the following functions

   (i) produces bile
  (ii) allows gaseous exchange
 (iii) secretes hydrochloric acid
 (iv) absorbs digested food
  (v) secretes a hormone
 (vi) stores and concentrates bile
(vii) contains a ciliated epithelium.

2. Food and Diet

Multiple Choice

In each of the following questions choose *one* only of the letters **A, B, C, D** or **E** to indicate your answer.

1   One gram of carbohydrate provides approximately

    A 8 kJ
    B 10 kJ
    C 12 kJ
    D 17 kJ
    E 25 kJ.

2   A carbohydrate such as starch is made up of units called

    A amino acids
    B disaccharides
    C monosaccharides
    D glycerides
    E peptides.

3   Which of the following foods does *not* contain appreciable quantities of protein?

    A cheese
    B steak
    C fish
    D fruit
    E beans.

4   Proteins are made up of units called

    A fatty acids
    B monosaccharides
    C peptones
    D amino acids
    E glycerides.

5   Kwashiorkor is a nutritional deficiency disease caused by

    A a lack of carbohydrate in the diet
    B a deficiency of certain minerals in the diet
    C a vitamin-deficient diet
    D insufficient roughage in the diet
    E insufficient protein in the diet.

6 Carrots contain appreciable quantities of

    A vitamin A
    B vitamin B
    C vitamin D
    D starch
    E glucose.

7 Which of the following vitamins is most readily destroyed during cooking?

    A B
    B A
    C D
    D C
    E K.

8 The importance of vitamins in the diet was discovered by

    A Pasteur
    B Hopkins
    C Bayliss and Starling
    D Koch
    E Fleming.

9 The two minerals required, in the diet, for bone formation are

    A calcium and iron
    B calcium and phosphorus
    C phosphorus and iodine
    D iodine and calcium
    E calcium and potassium.

10 Goitre is caused by a deficiency of

    A sodium
    B iron
    C calcium
    D iodine
    E potassium.

11 Iron is required in the diet

    A for the formation of tooth enamel
    B to produce thyroxine
    C to assist in wound healing
    D to produce haemoglobin
    E to assist in the production of strong bones.

12 When a green plant carries out photosynthesis

    A oxygen is used up
    B water is produced
    C the energy used comes from the breakdown of starch
    D nitrogen is given off by the leaves
    E carbon dioxide is used up.

The table below records the composition of six different foods.

FOOD (100 grams)	PROTEIN (grams)	FAT (grams)	CARBOHYDRATE (grams)	CALCIUM (milligrams)	VITAMIN A (micrograms)
1	17	8	0	7	120
2	3	4	5	120	8
3	6	1	86	4	0
4	1	0	19	7	20
5	12	12	0	56	60
6	12	50	0	11	0

Study the information in the table and then answer questions 13–15.

13 Which food has the highest energy value?

   A 1
   B 2
   C 3
   D 4
   E 6

14 Which food would provide the greatest quantity of bone-building material?

   A 1
   B 2
   C 3
   D 4
   E 5

15 Which food would cause the greatest increase in the blood glucose level?

   A 1
   B 2
   C 3
   D 4
   E 5

Multiple Completion

For each of the following incomplete statements or questions *one* or *more* of the responses numbered 1–4 are correct.

Choose the appropriate letter as your answer according to the following code

   A —if only 1, 2 and 3 are correct
   B —if only 1, 2 and 4 are correct
   C —if only 1 and 4 are correct
   D —if only 3 is correct
   E —if only 2, 3 and 4 are correct.

16 It is true to say of proteins that they

   1 are made up of units called monosaccharides
   2 do not need to be digested in the alimentary canal
   3 can be used to produce energy
   4 differ from one another only in the number of amino acids from which they are composed.

17 Vitamins are chemical compounds which

    1 have insignificant energy value in the body
    2 are required in the diet in very small amounts
    3 may be destroyed during cooking
    4 need to be digested in the alimentary canal.

18 Which of the following people may require extra iron in their diet?

    1 a pregnant woman
    2 an 18 year old youth
    3 a 13 year old boy
    4 a young woman with anaemia.

19 Which of the following is (are) true of a food chain?

    1 the sun's energy is fixed by green plants
    2 the biomass of consumers exceed the biomass of producers
    3 energy is not lost from the chain
    4 the energy fixed by plants is greater than that received by the carnivores.

20 It is true to say of milk that

    1 it contains calcium
    2 it contains several vitamins
    3 as a principal part of the diet it is unsuitable for adults because of its lack of
       iron
    4 it contains appreciable quantities of glucose.

Matching Pairs

Each set of questions consists of five lettered headings **A, B, C, D** and **E** followed by
four numbered items. Answer each question by choosing the *one* heading (**A, B, C, D**
or **E**) that is related most closely to the item concerned.

EACH HEADING MAY BE USED ONCE, MORE THAN ONCE OR NOT AT
ALL.

Questions 21–24

    A 9500 kJ
    B 11000 kJ
    C 12600 kJ
    D 14500 kJ
    E 17500 kJ.

Match the above energy requirements to the following people

21 housewife
22 female office worker
23 girl aged 12–14 years
24 male labourer.

Questions 25–28

Which of the following reagents

    A iodine solution
    B Millon's reagent
    C Benedict's (Fehling's) reagent
    D ethanol
    E dichlorophenol-indophenol (DCPIP)

can be used to test for

25 protein?
26 starch?
27 vitamin C?
28 glucose?

Questions 29–32

Which of the following diseases

    A anaemia
    B rickets
    C goitre
    D tooth decay
    E beri-beri

is caused by a deficiency of

29 vitamin B_1?
30 iodine?
31 iron?
32 vitamin D?

Questions 33–36

The pie charts in Fig 8 represent the nutrient content of five foods.

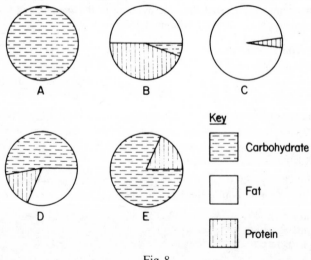

Fig. 8

Which of the charts could represent

33 peanuts
34 chocolate
35 butter
36 sugar?

Assertion/Reason

Each of the following questions consists of an *assertion* and a *reason*. Consider both statements and then choose the letter **A, B, C, D** or **E** as your answer according to the following

    A —if both statements are true, and the reason is a correct explanation of the assertion
    B —if both statements are true, but the reason is not a correct explanation of the assertion
    C —if the assertion is true, but the reason is false
    D —if the assertion is false, but the reason is true
    E —if both statements are false.

Code Summarized

	ASSERTION	REASON	
A	true	true	reason is a correct explanation
B	true	true	reason is not a correct explanation
C	true	false	
D	false	true	
E	false	false	

	ASSERTION		REASON
37	Fats are more easily digested than carbohydrates	*because*	fats have approximately twice the energy value of carbohydrates.
38	Vitamin D is an essential component of the diet	*because*	lack of vitamin D causes pellagra.
39	A pregnant woman requires extra calcium in the diet	*because*	the developing foetus requires calcium for bone formation.
40	A new-born baby is able to live solely on milk which contains no iron	*because*	the baby has stored iron while developing in the uterus.
41	A balanced diet should have adequate amounts of iodine	*because*	iodine is required for red blood cell production.
42	Fehling's or Benedict's reagent can be used to test for all sugars	*because*	a colour change takes place if sugars are present when tested with Fehling's or Benedict's reagent.

Structured Questions

43 a) State one reason for including each of the following in a diet and name two good sources of each.

    1 protein
    2 fat
    3 carbohydrate
    4 iron
    5 vitamin K
    6 water
    7 roughage.

    b) Name three nutritional deficiency diseases and state their cause.

44 Write short notes on each of the following

    a) iodised table salt
    b) addition of vitamins to certain foods
    c) milk as an ideal food
    d) the value of citrus fruits in the diet.

45

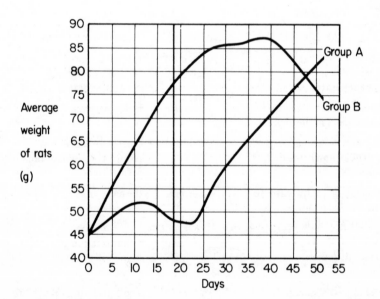

Fig. 9

16

Fig. 9 shows the growth of two groups of rats used in an experiment to determine the effects of diet on growth. Each group, A and B, received an identical diet consisting of carbohydrate, pure fat, casein, mineral salts and water. Group B was given a small amount of milk daily. After 18 days the milk was removed from the diet of group B and *added* to the diet of group A.

a) From the graph describe the growth of the rats in group A and B over the first 18 days of the experiment.
b) From the graph describe the effects of
   (i) removing the milk from the diet of group B
   (ii) adding the milk to the diet of group A.
c) Suggest a reason for your answer to (b) above.
d) Explain why two groups of rats were used instead of individual rats.
e) Explain, as fully as possible, the likely effects on the rats in group B of continuing the experiment for a further 30 days.

46 a) How do proteins differ in their chemical composition from carbohydrates and fats?
b) State six foods which are rich in protein.
c) Name two tests used to detect protein in food and describe how you would carry out one of the tests on a solid food material.

47 Several foods were tested for the presence of protein, reducing sugar and starch.

Some of the results are shown in the table below in terms of the colours produced during the tests.

FOOD	PROTEIN TEST	STARCH TEST	REDUCING SUGAR TEST
Milk	Red/violet	Brown	Red
Potatoes	Clear colour		
Cheese		Brown	Blue
Table sugar	Clear colour		
Fish		Brown	Blue

a) Name the tests you would use to test for protein, reducing sugar and starch.
b) Complete the table for potatoes, cheese, table sugar and fish by writing in the appropriate colour.
c) From the results, describe the nutrient content of the five foods.
d) Name two foods from the table which would give a positive result if tested for fat.
e) Describe how you would carry out a fat test on a solid food.

48 The table below shows the energy requirement per day for various people.

PERSON	ENERGY REQUIREMENT PER DAY (kilojoules)
Coal miner	
11 year old boy	10,500
Athlete in training	19,000
Typist	10,500
2 year old child	
Nursing mother	

a) Complete the table.
b) State four factors which decide a person's daily energy requirement.
c) A person asleep for 8 hours requires 2500 kJ. to maintain his basal metabolism. If he sleeps for 16 hours of a day and then spends the remaining 8 hours watching television, how many kilojoules will he require that day?
d) In the diet of a European which foods generally provide the main sources of energy?

3. Nutrition and Digestion

Multiple Choice

In each of the following questions choose *one* only of the letters **A, B, C, D** or **E** to indicate your answer.

1   The enzyme which curdles milk is called

    A trypsin
    B lipase
    C amylase
    D rennin
    E pepsin.

2   The enzyme pepsin

    A converts fats to fatty acids and glycerol
    B converts starch to maltose
    C digests proteins into amino acids
    D digests proteins into polypeptides
    E converts maltose to glucose.

3   An enzyme which requires very acid conditions is produced in the

    A stomach
    B pancreas
    C duodenum
    D ileum
    E oesophagus.

4   Protein digestion begins in the

    A mouth
    B ileum
    C colon
    D oesophagus
    E stomach.

5   Digestion of fats results in the formation of

    A amino acids
    B glucose
    C glycerol and fatty acids
    D glucose and fructose
    E polypeptides.

6   Which of the following is *not* a function of the small intestine?

    A absorption of vitamins and minerals
    B absorption of amino acids
    C production of a fat-digesting enzyme
    D production of a carbohydrate-digesting enzyme
    E absorption of water.

7   Tooth decay is caused mainly by

   A bacteria attacking the enamel
   B food which is abrasive
   C acids produced by bacteria
   D fluoridated toothpaste
   E acidic foods such as pickles and vinegar.

8   The surface of a tooth is covered with

   A dentine
   B cement
   C a peridontal membrane
   D enamel
   E plaque.

9   Which of the following is *not* a function of the liver?

   A production of bile
   B storage of some vitamins
   C storage of glycogen
   D deamination of amino acids
   E removal of urea from the blood.

10   Bile is produced by the

   A pancreas
   B gall bladder
   C duodenum
   D bile duct
   E liver.

11   Which of the following glands does *not* produce enzymes?

   A salivary glands
   B gastric glands
   C pancreas
   D intestinal glands
   E thyroid.

12   The oesophagus connects the

   A mouth and lungs
   B throat and lungs
   C pancreas and duodenum
   D stomach and mouth
   E gall bladder and duodenum.

13   Which of the following is an *incorrect* statement concerning the stomach?

   A it produces rennin
   B it stores food
   C it receives alkaline food from the mouth
   D alcohol is absorbed through the stomach walls
   E it produces a carbohydrate-digesting enzyme.

Multiple Completion

For each of the following incomplete statements or questions *one* or *more* of the responses numbered 1–4 are correct.

Choose the appropriate letter as your answer according to the following code

A —if only 1, 2 and 3 are correct
B —if only 1, 2 and 4 are correct
C —if only 1 and 4 are correct
D —if only 3 is correct
E —if only 2, 3 and 4 are correct.

14 Which of the following enzymes require(s) alkaline conditions?

1 pepsin
2 amylase
3 lipase
4 trypsin.

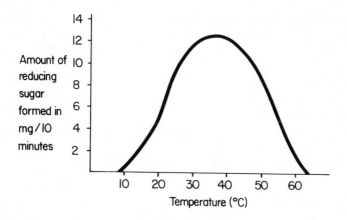

Fig. 10

Fig. 10 above shows the effect of temperature on the breakdown of starch to reducing sugar by the enzyme salivary amylase.

15 Which of the following conclusions may safely be drawn from the graph above?

1 The optimum temperature for this enzyme is 37°C.
2 The amount of reducing sugar formed is the same at 24°C and 50°C.
3 At 30°C the rate of reaction is twice that at 20°C.
4 Above 45°C the rate of reaction falls off rapidly.

16 Hydrochloric acid secreted in the stomach

1 kills bacteria taken in with the food
2 provides the optimum pH for the enzyme pepsin
3 inactivates amylase produced in the mouth
4 inactivates rennin.

17 Digestion of food is dependent upon

1 action of specific enzymes
2 presence of villi in the small intestine
3 production of a hormone from the pancreas
4 maintenance of suitable pH conditions.

18 Excess glucose is converted to glycogen and stored in the

1 liver
2 kidneys
3 bones
4 muscles.

19 The digestion of maltose may take place in the

1 stomach
2 mouth
3 small intestine
4 duodenum.

20 In which of the following does peristalsis *not* take place?

1 oesophagus
2 duodenum
3 mouth
4 colon.

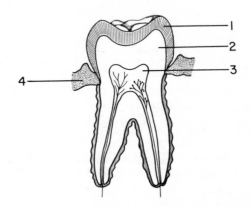

Fig. 11

Study Fig. 11 above and then answer questions 21 and 22.

21 Which of the following numbered parts contain living cells?

1 2
2 4
3 1
4 3.

22 The structure numbered 3 contains

  1 blood capillaries
  2 nerve endings
  3 connective tissue
  4 bone.

23 Which of the following is (are) *not* true of the alimentary canal?

  1 The duodenum receives bile directly from the liver.
  2 The colon does not produce enzymes.
  3 Amylase is produced in the mouth.
  4 Absorption of digested food takes place in the stomach.

Matching Pairs

Each set of questions consists of five lettered headings, **A, B, C, D** and **E** followed by four numbered items. Answer each question by choosing the *one* heading (**A, B, C, D** or **E**) that is related most closely to the item concerned.

EACH HEADING MAY BE USED ONCE, MORE THAN ONCE OR NOT AT ALL.

Questions 24–27

Which of the following structures

  A salivary glands
  B pancreas
  C stomach
  D small intestine
  E liver

produces

24 bile?
25 trypsin?
26 rennin?
27 pepsin?

Questions 28–31

Which of the following substrates

  A starch
  B protein
  C cellulose
  D fat
  E maltose

is broken down by

28 amylase (ptyalin)?
29 lipase?
30 pepsin?
31 maltase?

Questions 32–35

Which of the following functions

    A storage of glycogen
    B absorption of water
    C storage of bile
    D production of hydrochloric acid
    E absorption of amino acids

is carried out by

32 the liver?
33 the gall bladder?
34 the colon?
35 the small intestine?

Assertion/Reason

Each of the following questions consists of an *assertion* and a *reason*. Consider both statements and then choose the letter **A, B, C, D** or **E** as your answer according to the following

    A —if both statements are true, and the reason is a correct explanation of the assertion
    B —if both statements are true, but the reason is not a correct explanation of the assertion
    C —if the assertion is true, but the reason is false
    D —if the assertion is false, but the reason is true
    E —if both statements are false.

Code Summarized

	ASSERTION	REASON	
A	true	true	reason is a correct explanation
B	true	true	reason is not a correct explanation
C	true	false	
D	false	true	
E	false	false	

	ASSERTION		REASON
36	Proteins are not digested by trypsin	*because*	trypsin is a fat digesting enzyme.
37	Enzymes do not function at high temperatures	*because*	all enzymes are proteins which are inactivated by high temperatures.
38	Saliva is secreted in the mouth when eating	*because*	the presence of food triggers off a reflex action causing increased production of saliva.
39	Tooth decay often causes pain	*because*	the pulp cavity contains blood capillaries.
40	The pH of the duodenum is acidic	*because*	pancreatic enzymes function best in acidic conditions.

24

41

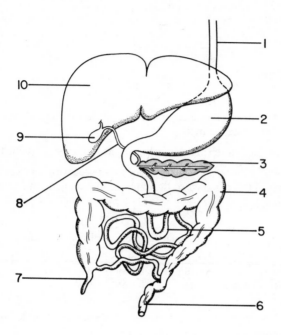

Fig. 12

a) Name the parts numbered 1–10 in Fig. 12.
b) Mark with a letter P, on the diagram, the position of the pyloric sphincter.
c) What is the function of the pyloric sphincter?
d) Mark with a letter L, on the diagram, the organ in which the Islets of Langerhans are found.
e) Name the substance produced by the Islets of Langerhans.
f) In which numbered structure is bile produced?
g) In which numbered structure is pepsin produced?
h) What is the function of pepsin?
i) Mark with a letter A, on the diagram, the organ in which absorption of amino acids occurs.
j) Name the blood vessel carrying digested food to the liver.
k) State what happens in the liver to excessive amounts of

  (i) glucose
  (ii) amino acids.

42

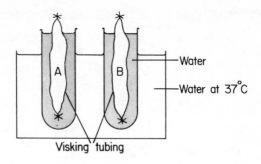

Fig. 13

The apparatus shown in Fig. 13 was set up to demonstrate the effect of digestion and absorption in the alimentary canal.

Both A and B contained starch and water, *one* of the tubes also contained an enzyme.

The water *surrounding* the bags of visking tubing was tested with iodine and Fehling's (or Benedict's) reagent at the start of the experiment and again after 30 minutes.

The results are shown in the table.

	IODINE TEST		FEHLING'S TEST	
	A	B	A	B
At start	Brown	Brown	Blue	Blue
After 30 mins.		Brown	Red	

a) Complete the table for A after 30 minutes and B after 30 minutes by writing in the appropriate colour.
b) Which tube contained an enzyme?
c) Name the enzyme.
d) What substance was present in the water surrounding the visking tubing bag A after 30 minutes?
e) What does the water surrounding the visking tubing represent in the digestive system?
f) What conclusions can you draw regarding the permeability of the visking tubing to starch?
g) What is the purpose of tube B?
h) The pH inside the bags A and B was maintained at pH 7.5. How would you expect the results to differ if the experiment was repeated at pH 3.0?
i) Describe how you would carry out a Fehling's or Benedict's test.

43 An experiment was carried out to determine the effect of enzymes present in saliva and an extract from the pancreas on starch. Four tubes were set up containing the substances shown in the table

TUBE	CONTENTS
1	5 cm^3 starch suspension + 5 cm^3 saliva
2	5 cm^3 starch suspension + 5 cm^3 boiled saliva
3	5 cm^3 starch suspension + 5 cm^3 pancreatin
4	5 cm^3 starch suspension + 5 cm^3 boiled pancreatin

a) At which temperature would you incubate the tubes? Why?
b) Describe a suitable arrangement for incubation of the tubes.
c) At 1 minute intervals drops of liquid were removed from each of the four tubes and added to separate drops of iodine solution on a spotting tile. What was the purpose of this procedure?
d) After 3 minutes a sample from tube 1 was added to iodine and gave a brown colour. What does this indicate regarding the contents of tube 1?
e) Tubes 2 and 4 gave a blue-black colour on addition to iodine. What does this indicate regarding the contents of these two tubes?
f) Tube 3 gave a brown colour on addition to iodine. Which of the four tubes contained an *active* starch-digesting enzyme?
g) Name the enzymes.
h) After 10 minutes samples from all four tubes were tested for the presence of reducing sugar. Describe how you would carry out this test. What results would you expect in the four tubes?
i) Explain the effect of boiling on the enzymes.

44

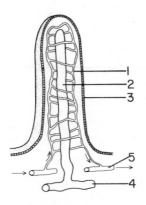

Fig. 14

Fig. 14 represents a section of a villus. (The arrows indicate the direction of blood flow)

a) In which part of the alimentary canal are villi found?
b) Name the structures numbered 1–4.
c) Into which numbered structure do calcium, iron and vitamin A pass during absorption?
d) Into which numbered structure do the products of fat digestion pass?
e) Name two features of villi which make them suitable for the absorption of digested food.
f) To which major blood vessel does the structure numbered 5 lead?

45 A student carried out the following experiment to determine the effect of an extract from the pancreas on a food substance present in milk.

He set up three test tubes containing the substances shown in the table. Bromo-Thymol blue is an indicator which changes colour from blue in alkaline solution to yellow in acid solution. The tubes were kept in a water bath at 37° C and the time taken for the colour to change from blue to yellow was noted.

TUBE	CONTENTS	TIME FOR COLOUR CHANGE
1	Milk, bromo-thymol blue, sodium hydroxide, pancreatin	6 minutes
2	Milk, bromo-thymol blue, bile salts sodium hydroxide, boiled pancreatin	No change
3	Milk, bromo-thymol blue, bile salts, sodium hydroxide, pancreatin	2 minutes

Consider the information above and answer the following questions.

   a) Which substance present in milk was being digested?
   b) Pancreatin contains several enzymes. Name the one responsible for the above changes.
   c) Sodium hydroxide is an alkali. What was the colour of the tubes at the start of the experiment?
   d) What was the colour of the tubes at the end of the experiment?
   e) What was the pH of the tubes at the end of the experiment?
   f) What caused the colour change in the indicator?
   g) Why did tube 3 change colour more quickly than tube 1?
   h) What was the purpose of the bile salts in this experiment?
   i) Why did boiled pancreatin cause no colour change?

46 Colon, ascorbic acid, amino acids, rectum, thiamine, glucose, assimilation, deamination, chyme, chyle, pyloric sphincter, glycerol, pellagra, rickets, pancreas, peristalsis, liver, duodenum, ileum, villus, lipase, amylase.

From the list above choose the correct term for each of the following

   a) large intestine
   b) product of starch digestion
   c) material leaving the stomach
   d) breakdown of amino acids in the liver
   e) a deficiency disease caused by lack of vitamin D
   f) product of fat digestion
   g) a structure which closes the exit from the stomach
   h) an enzyme present in saliva
   i) a structure which secretes enzymes into the duodenum
   j) a structure which increases the surface area of the small intestine
   k) an organ which stores glycogen
   l) small intestine
   m) a region of the alimentary canal which receives bile
   n) waves of muscular contraction in the alimentary canal
   o) a vitamin found in lemons.

4. Respiration

Multiple Choice

In each of the following questions choose *one* only of the letters **A, B, C, D** or **E** to indicate your answer.

1 The normal substrate in cellular respiration is

   A sucrose
   B glycogen
   C glucose
   D fat
   E protein.

2 The concentration of oxygen in expired air is approximately

   A 0%
   B 12.5%
   C 14%
   D 16%
   E 21%

3 Carbon dioxide is transported in the blood to the lungs as

   A gas bubbles in the plasma
   B bicarbonate ions
   C carboxyhaemoglobin
   D oxyhaemoglobin
   E carbonic anhydrase.

4 The products of cellular respiration are

   A oxygen, carbon dioxide and water
   B urea, carbon dioxide and water
   C ATP, carbon dioxide and water
   D ATP, oxygen and urea
   E ATP, urea and water.

5 In which of the following does gaseous exchange by diffusion take place?

   A alveolar ducts
   B alveoli
   C bronchioles
   D bronchi
   E trachea.

6 The air expired from the lungs

   A contains less carbon dioxide than inspired air
   B contains no oxygen
   C contains no carbon dioxide
   D contains carbon dioxide and nitrogen only
   E contains approximately 3% carbon dioxide.

7   Oxygen is transported around the body in the

   A tissue fluid
   B white blood cells
   C red blood cells
   D plasma
   E platelets.

8   An oxygen debt is incurred when

   A there is excess carbon dioxide in the body
   B nitrogen bubbles form in the blood
   C ATP production exceeds demand
   D alcohol is formed instead of carbon dioxide and water in the cells
   E gaseous exchange cannot keep pace with oxygen requirements.

9   The rate of breathing is largely controlled by the

   A concentration of carbon dioxide in the blood
   B concentration of urea in the blood
   C blood pressure
   D lung capacity
   E concentration of oxygen in the blood.

10   The function of respiration is to

   A produce carbon dioxide
   B take in oxygen during breathing
   C remove excess water
   D produce useful energy
   E produce heat to maintain the body temperature.

11   The alveolar walls are moist so that

   A germs are trapped
   B water vapour can be expired
   C oxygen can dissolve
   D air can diffuse from the blood
   E carbon dioxide cannot dissolve.

12   During breathing movements, which of the following is directly responsible for causing air to enter the lungs?

   A muscular movements of the diaphragm suck air in
   B the intercostal muscles cause air to be drawn in
   C the lungs are elastic and expand
   D the trachea expands to allow air in
   E the air pressure in the lungs is lowered below atmospheric pressure.

13 Through which of the following blood vessels does oxygenated blood leave the lungs?

    A pulmonary artery
    B pulmonary vein
    C dorsal aorta
    D superior vena cava
    E carotid artery.

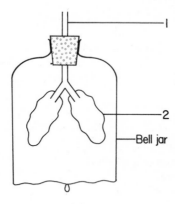

Fig. 15

Fig. 15 shows a model often used to demonstrate the action of breathing. Study this diagram and then answer questions 14–16.

14 The part numbered 2 represents the

    A pleura
    B diaphragm
    C alveoli
    D intercostal muscles
    E lungs.

15 Which part of the thorax is represented by the bell jar?

    A pleural membranes
    B ribs and intercostal muscles
    C pericardium
    D pleural cavity
    E diaphragm

16 The part numbered 1 represents the

    A bronchi
    B trachea
    C oesophagus
    D bronchioles
    E ribs.

Multiple Completion

For each of the following incomplete statements or questions *one,* or *more* of the responses numbered 1–4 are correct.

Choose the appropriate letter as your answer according to the following code

A —if only 1, 2 and 3 are correct
B —if only 1, 2 and 4 are correct
C —if only 1 and 4 are correct
D —if only 3 is correct
E —if only 2, 3 and 4 are correct.

17 Anaerobic respiration in man produces

1 lactic acid
2 alcohol
3 glycogen
4 energy.

18 When respiration takes place in a cell

1 energy is released through ATP
2 the cell gains in weight
3 carbon dioxide is used up and oxygen released
4 energy is released as heat.

19 Which of the following is (are) necessary for ATP production?

1 a supply of ADP
2 a supply of glucose
3 a supply of carbon dioxide
4 a supply of inorganic phosphate.

20 During vigorous exercise

1 glycogen reserves decrease
2 ATP is produced
3 lactic acid is used up in the muscles
4 an oxygen debt is built up.

21 Efficient gaseous exchange in the lungs is dependent upon

1 movement of the ribs and diaphragm
2 an efficient blood supply to the lungs
3 the nitrogen concentration of the blood
4 the carbon dioxide concentration of the blood.

22 As air passes from the external atmosphere to the alveoli

1 it is warmed
2 oxygen is extracted from it
3 carbon dioxide is added to it
4 foreign particles such as dust are removed.

23 Which of the following is (are) correct statements concerning breathing?

1 The amount of air breathed at rest is termed the tidal volume.
2 The average breathing rate is 16 breaths per minute.
3 The amount of air expelled by the deepest breath is termed the vital capacity.
4 The amount of air breathed at rest is approximately 4 litres per minute.

24 When oxygen passes from the atmosphere to combine with haemoglobin it passes through

1 alveolar membranes
2 blood plasma
3 capillary walls
4 bronchial walls.

25 Which of the following is (are) air conducting passages?

1 epiglottis
2 bronchus
3 trachea
4 bronchiole.

Matching Pairs

Each set of questions consists of five lettered headings A, B, C, D and E followed
by four numbered items. Answer each question by choosing the *one* heading (A, B, C,
D or E) that is related most closely to the item concerned.

EACH HEADING MAY BE USED ONCE, MORE THAN ONCE OR NOT AT
ALL.

Questions 26–29

A ATP
B oxygen
C haemoglobin
D cell enzymes
E glucose

Which of the above is

26 involved in oxygen transport?

27 a red pigment containing iron?

28 transported to the cells in the plasma?

29 a temporary store of energy?

Questions 30–33

A vital capacity
B tidal volume
C residual volume
D expiratory reserve volume
E ventilation rate

Which of the above terms is applied to

30   the volume of air breathed per minute?
31   the amount of air that can be expired after a maximum inspiration?
32   the volume of air remaining in the lungs after maximum expiration?
33   the volume of air taken into the lungs when breathing normally at rest?

Questions 34–37

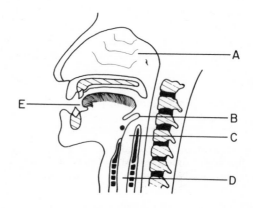

Fig. 16

Match the lettered structures in Fig. 16 above to the following

34   an area where air is warmed and moistened
35   a structure which closes the entrance to the trachea
36   a structure supported by C-shaped rings of cartilage
37   the position of vocal cords.

Questions 38–41

Which of the structures labelled A–E in Fig. 17

38   represents the trachea?
39   is covered by a pleural membrane?
40   is a bronchiole?
41   represents the structures which prevent closure of the trachea during breathing?

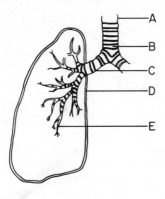

Fig. 17

Assertion/Reason

Each of the following questions consists of an *assertion* and a *reason*. Consider both statements and then choose the letter **A, B, C, D** or **E** as your answer according to the following

    A —if both statements are true, and the reason is a correct explanation of the assertion

    B —if both statements are true, but the reason is not a correct explanation of the assertion

    C —if the assertion is true, but the reason is false

    D —if the assertion is false, but the reason is true

    E —if both statements are false.

Code Summarized

	ASSERTION	REASON	
A	true	true	reason is a correct explanation
B	true	true	reason is not a correct explanation
C	true	false	
D	false	true	
E	false	false	

	ASSERTION		REASON
42	All the energy produced by respiration is converted to ATP	*because*	ATP is the substance in which energy is temporarily stored.
43	Oxygen diffuses from the alveoli to the blood	*because*	the oxygen concentration in the blood is lower than in the alveoli.

ASSERTION		REASON
44 Carbon monoxide is a poisonous gas	*because*	carbon monoxide combines with haemoglobin and prevents the carriage of oxygen.
45 Expired air has a higher concentration of carbon dioxide than inspired air	*because*	carbon dioxide is produced during respiration.
46 When the neck is bent the trachea closes	*because*	the rings of cartilage on the trachea are incomplete.

Structured Questions

47 a) Explain how ventilation of the lungs is brought about.
   b) Describe and explain the effect on the breathing rate of

   (i) exercise
   (ii) reduction in the oxygen concentration of the air from 20% to 15%.

48 a) Name three features of the human lungs which make them suitable sites for gaseous exchange.
   b) Define respiration using all of the following terms:–
   carbon dioxide, oxygen, ATP, cells, mitochondria, glucose, water.
   c) List, in order, the structures through which a molecule of oxygen would pass in travelling from the external atmosphere to a kidney cell.

49 The figures below show the variations in the blood sugar concentration of an athlete before, during and after a race.

Time (p.m.)	Blood sugar concentration (mg/100 cm³)
12.30	90
1.00	90
1.30	90
2.00	95
2.30	120
3.00	92
3.30	75
4.00	82
4.30	90
5.00	90

   a) Plot a graph of these figures.
   b) What is the normal blood sugar concentration for this subject?
   c) From the graph read off

   (i) the highest sugar level
   (ii) the lowest sugar level.

   d) The race began at 2.30 and lasted for one hour. From the graph read off the blood sugar levels

   (i) half-way through the race
   (ii) at the end of the race
   (iii) 90 minutes after the start of the race.

e) How many minutes after the end of the race did it take for the blood sugar concentration to return to its original level?
f) At 1.00 the athlete took several glucose tablets by mouth

    (i) what effect does this have on his blood sugar concentration and what causes it?
    (ii) what is the athlete's purpose in taking these tablets?

g) What causes the large decrease in the blood sugar concentration between 2.30 and 3.30?
h) Explain why the blood sugar level does not fall below $75\,mg/100\,cm^3$.
i) Explain, in detail, the mechanisms responsible for maintaining the levels of blood sugar.

50 The table below gives figures to show the effects of walking at various speeds.

SPEED (km/hour)	NUMBER OF BREATHS (per minute)	VOLUME OF EACH BREATH (litres)	VOLUME OF AIR BREATHED PER MINUTE (litres)
2		0.8	12.0
5	−17	1.6	
7	19		38.0
9		2.5	50.0

a) Work out the number of breaths per minute at 2 and 9 km/hour, the volume of each breath at 7 km/hour and the volume of air breathed per minute at 5 km/hour. Use these figures to complete the table.
b) How much more air per breath did the subject take in when walking at 9 km/hour than at 2 km/hour?
c) How much more air per minute did the subject breathe when walking at 9 km/hour than at 2 km/hour?
d) Give a reason for the difference in (c) above.
e) Plot a graph of the volume of air breathed per minute at the four speeds.

5. Blood and Circulation

Multiple Choice

In each of the following questions choose *one* only of the letters **A, B, C, D** or **E** to indicate your answer.

1 The element necessary for haemoglobin formation is

   A copper
   B iron
   C iodine
   D magnesium
   E potassium.

2 The approximate life of a red blood cell is

   A two days
   B two weeks
   C two months
   D one week
   E four months.

3 Red blood cells are produced in the

   A spleen
   B liver
   C kidneys
   D heart
   E bone marrow.

4 Blood pressure is measured using a (an)

   A haemocytometer
   B electro-cardiogram
   C electro-encephalograph
   D sphygmomanometer
   E stethoscope.

5 Red blood cells have a short lifetime and they are broken down by the

   A spleen
   B bone marrow
   C kidneys
   D stomach
   E heart.

6 Which of the following is *not* a function of the blood?

   A transport of heat around the body
   B clotting to prevent loss of blood
   C transport of hormones
   D destruction of pathogenic bacteria
   E production of hormones.

7   Sugar is transported in the blood in the form of

   A   glucose
   B   fructose
   C   maltose
   D   sucrose
   E   a mixture of the above.

8   Which of the following is a function of white blood cells?

   A   transport of oxygen
   B   transport of carbon dioxide
   C   assistance in blood clotting
   D   production of antibodies
   E   transport of hormones.

9   Which of the following is an *incorrect* statement concerning the difference between the blood in the renal artery and renal vein?

   A   there is less oxygen in the renal vein
   B   there is less urea in the renal vein
   C   there is more carbon dioxide in the renal vein
   D   there is more oxygen in the renal vein
   E   there is more glucose in the renal artery.

10   Blood clotting may be prevented by the addition of

   A   calcium ions
   B   sodium chloride
   C   sodium citrate
   D   thrombokinase
   E   fibrinogen.

11   Which of the following contains oxygenated blood?

   A   posterior vena cava
   B   right atrium (auricle)
   C   right ventricle
   D   renal vein
   E   pulmonary vein.

12   Which of the following organs has a vein leaving it and a vein and artery supplying it?

   A   liver
   B   brain
   C   kidney
   D   spleen
   E   heart.

13 The only artery which carries deoxygenated blood is the

    A renal artery
    B femoral artery
    C subclavian artery
    D pulmonary artery
    E hepatic artery.

14 To which of the blood vessels listed below does the following description apply? It is found in the abdominal cavity, it carries blood to the liver and contains a relatively large amount of glucose, amino acids and carbon dioxide.

    A hepatic vein
    B renal vein
    C posterior vena cava
    D aorta
    E hepatic portal vein.

15 A universal donor is of blood group

    A AB
    B A
    C B
    D Rhesus positive
    E O.

16 The liquid which bathes all living cells is called

    A serum
    B plasma
    C tissue fluid
    D mucus
    E vitreous humour.

Multiple Completion

For each of the following incomplete statements or questions *one* or *more* of the responses numbered 1–4 are correct.

Choose the appropriate letter as your answer according to the following code

    A —if only 1, 2 and 3 are correct
    B —if only 1, 2 and 4 are correct
    C —if only 1 and 4 are correct
    D —if only 3 is correct
    E —if only 2, 3 and 4 are correct.

17 It is true to say of arteries that they

    1 always carry oxygenated blood
    2 contain elastic fibres in their walls
    3 take blood away from the heart
    4 have thicker walls than veins.

18 The chamber(s) of the heart which contain(s) oxygenated blood is (are) the

1 left atrium
2 right atrium
3 right ventricle
4 left ventricle.

19 Coronary heart disease may be caused by

1 a blood clot in the coronary artery
2 a high level of fat in the diet
3 an inherited condition
4 smoking.

20 A person of blood group AB can receive blood from a person of blood group

1 O only
2 AB
3 B
4 A.

21 A person of blood group A can donate blood to a person of group

1 A
2 O
3 B
4 AB.

22 Which of the following statements is (are) true of lymph nodes?

1 they produce lymphocytes
2 they filter bacteria from the lymph
3 they produce red cells
4 they may swell as a result of infection.

Matching Pairs

Each set of questions consists of five lettered headings **A, B, C, D** and **E** followed by four numbered items. Answer each question by choosing the *one* heading (**A, B, C, D** or **E**) that is related most closely to the item concerned.

EACH HEADING MAY BE USED ONCE, MORE THAN ONCE OR NOT AT ALL.

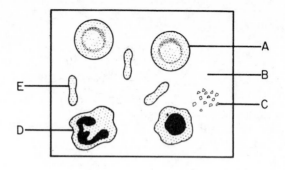

Fig. 18

Figure 18 shows a sample of human blood. Which of the structures labelled A–E

23 represents the plasma?
24 contains the protein fibrinogen?
25 transports amino acids?
26 is able to ingest bacteria?

Questions 27–30

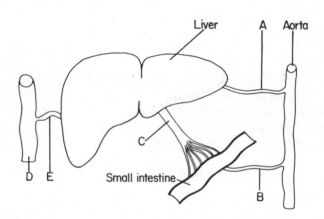

Fig. 19

Which of the structures labelled A–E in Fig. 19

27 carries deoxygenated blood to the heart?
28 carries blood rich in glucose and amino acids?
29 is the hepatic vein?
30 is the inferior vena cava?

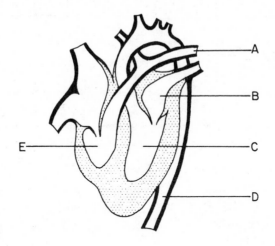

Fig. 20

Which of the structures labelled A–E in Fig. 20

31 carries deoxygenated blood to the lungs?

32 pumps blood to the lungs?

33 represents the aorta?

34 receives oxygenated blood from the lungs?

Assertion/Reason

Each of the following questions consists of an *assertion* and a *reason*. Consider both statements and then choose the letter **A, B, C, D** or **E** as your ansser according to the following

    A —if both statements are true, and the reason is a correct explanation of the assertion

    B —if both statements are true, but the reason is not a correct explanation of the assertion

    C —if the assertion is true, but the reason is false

    D —if the assertion is false, but the reason is true

    E —if both statements are false.

Code Summarized

	ASSERTION	REASON	
A	true	true	reason is a correct explanation
B	true	true	reason is not a correct explanation
C	true	false	
D	false	true	
E	false	false	

ASSERTION		REASON
35 Blood in an artery is bright red	because	arterial blood contains oxyhaemoglobin.
36 People who live at high altitudes have more red cells than people who live at sea level	because	the oxygen concentration at high altitudes is greater than at sea level.
37 Arteries assist the flow of blood	because	arteries have elastic tissue in their walls.
38 Blood pressure in veins is greater than in arteries	because	veins contain valves.
39 Plasma passes out of a capillary	because	the capillaries increase the rate of flow of the blood.
40 Lymph flows in one direction only	because	the lymph nodes pump the lymph through the lymphatic vessels.

Structured Questions

41   The following substances may be found in the blood of a healthy person

    1   urea
    2   lactic acid
    3   glucose
    4   carbon dioxide
    5   antibodies.

   a) For each substance state

      (i) its origin
      (ii) its destination
      (iii) the reason why it is found in the blood.

   b) State a particular circumstance in which the levels of the above substances may be particularly high and name a blood vessel likely to contain a high level of the substance.

42   a) Describe two ways in which the blood protects the body from disease.
     b) State three differences between the composition of the blood in the hepatic portal vein and the hepatic vein.
     c) By means of labelled diagrams describe the difference in structure between red and white blood cells.

43 The diagram below shows a plan of part of the blood circulation.

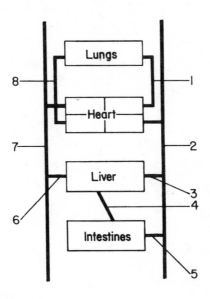

Fig. 21

a) Name the blood vessels numbered 1–8 in Fig. 21.

b) Give the numbers of those blood vessels which contain oxygenated blood.

c) Name the four chambers of the heart.

d) Which two chambers contain deoxygenated blood?

e) Draw an arrow alongside the blood vessels numbered 1, 2, 4 and 8 to indicate the direction of blood flow in those vessels.

f) Explain what is meant by the double circulation of the blood.

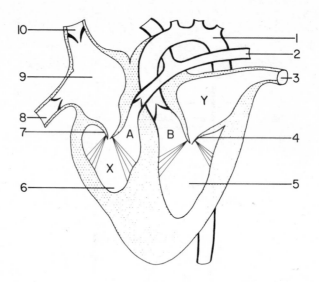

Fig. 22

a) Name the structures numbered 1–10 in Fig. 22.
b) State whether the blood at points X and Y is oxygenated or deoxygenated.
c) Using arrows, mark on the diagram, the direction of blood flow at points A and B.
d) Give one function of each of the following

   (i) plasma
   (ii) platelets
   (iii) white blood cells.

45 a) Consider the following information relating to blood transfusion

   (i) group O is a 'universal donor'
   (ii) group AB is a 'universal recipient'
   (iii) a person may receive blood of his own group.

Now complete the following table, indicating by a tick (√) where no agglutination (clumping) will occur and by a cross (✕) where agglutination will occur.

	Recipient			
Donor	O	A	B	AB
O				
A				
B				
AB				

b) Explain the terms 'universal donor' and 'universal recipient'.

46 Write short notes on each of the following

    a) blood clotting
    b) the pulse
    c) lymph nodes
    d) blood transfusion.

47 Three test-tubes were prepared containing $10\,cm^3$ of the following solutions

    A contained distilled water
    B contained 0.9% sodium chloride solution
    C contained 5.0% sodium chloride solution.
    (0.9% sodium chloride is isotonic with human blood)

To each tube was added several drops of defibrinated human blood and the tubes were left for 15 minutes.

The tubes were then examined and the following observations made.

Tube A was a clear red solution and on examination under the microscope no red blood cells could be seen.

Tube B contained a suspension with normal blood cells present.

Tube C also contained a suspension with red blood cells present.

    a) What is defibrinated blood?
    b) Why is it necessary to use this type of blood?
    c) Explain why no red blood cells could be found in tube A.
    d) What caused the clear red solution in tube A?
    e) Explain why normal red blood cells could be seen in tube B.
    f) Draw a diagram to show the shape of a normal red blood cell and the shape of the blood cells in tube C.
    g) Name the process responsible for the changes in tubes A and C.

6. Excretion and the Skin

Multiple Choice

In each of the following questions choose *one* only of the letters **A, B, C, D** or **E** to indicate your answer.

1 Urine passes from the kidney to the bladder through the

    A ureter
    B urethra
    C uterus
    D rectum
    E vas deferens.

2 Which of the following structures is *not* found in the cortex of the kidney?

    A Bowman's capsule
    B afferent blood vessel
    C first convoluted tubule
    D loop of Henle
    E second convoluted tubule.

3 The fluid found in Bowman's capsule contains

    A urine
    B blood plasma and blood cells
    C urea and glucose only
    D the same materials as found in blood plasma
    E the same materials as found in blood plasma except proteins.

4 The fluid found in Bowman's capsule is derived from the blood. This fluid is formed by a process of

    A hydrostatic pressure
    B diffusion
    C osmosis
    D active transport
    E ultra-filtration.

5 In which of the following parts of the kidney tubule does reabsorption of glucose occur?

    A first convoluted tubule
    B second convoluted tubule
    C collecting duct
    D Bowman's capsule
    E loop of Henle.

6 Anti-diuretic hormone regulates the activity of the kidney. In which gland is it produced?

A pituitary gland
B thyroid gland
C adrenal gland
D testes
E thymus gland.

7 Which of the following is a function of the kidney?

A manufacture of urea
B breakdown of amino acids
C assistance in temperature regulation of the body
D excretion of glucose
E regulation of the water content of the body.

8 Which of the following substances, present in blood plasma, is not normally found in the fluid in Bowman's capsule?

A proteins
B urea
C water
D glucose
E sodium salts.

9 Urea is formed from the breakdown of

A glucose
B amino acids
C cholesterol
D fat
E ammonia.

10 The removal from the body of metabolic waste products is termed

A egestion
B secretion
C digestion
D defaecation
E excretion.

11 Which of the following would assist in heat loss?

A vaso-dilation
B the insulating properties of adipose tissue
C wearing thick woollen clothing
D direction of blood from the skin to the internal organs
E shivering.

12 Which of the following vitamins can be produced by the action of sunlight on the skin?

A C
B D
C B
D K
E A.

13 The primary purpose of sweating is to

A increase the body temperature
B lower the body temperature
C remove excess water
D kill bacteria on the skin
E remove salt from the body.

14 Which of the following is a response to cold?

A increase in sweating
B fall in metabolic rate
C dilation of blood capillaries in the skin
D lowering of hairs
E rapid contraction and relaxation of skeletal muscles.

Multiple Completion

For each of the following incomplete statements or questions *one* or *more* of the responses numbered 1–4 are correct.

Choose the appropriate letter as your answer according to the following code

A —if only 1, 2 and 3 are correct
B —if only 1, 2 and 4 are correct
C —if only 1 and 4 are correct
D —if only 3 is correct
E —if only 2, 3 and 4 are correct.

15 Which of the following organs excrete water from the body?

1 lungs
2 spleen
3 liver
4 skin.

16 Products of metabolism include

1 faeces
2 water
3 carbon dioxide
4 urea.

17 In a normally functioning kidney

1 glucose is reabsorbed into the blood
2 over 95% of the water in the nephron is reabsorbed
3 urea passes into the collecting duct
4 proteins are filtered into the nephron and later reabsorbed.

18 Which of the following skin structures assist in temperature regulation?

1 adipose tissue
2 cornified layer
3 sebaceous gland
4 blood capillaries.

19 A hot, humid atmosphere may lead to

1 failure of sweat to evaporate from the skin
2 heat stagnation
3 increased metabolic rate
4 overheating of the body.

20 The condition hypothermia is

1 characterised by a rapid fall in body temperature
2 often caused by exposure to cold, wet conditions
3 never fatal
4 more common in elderly people.

Matching Pairs

Each set of questions consists of five lettered headings **A, B, C, D** and **E** followed by four numbered items. Answer each question by choosing the *one* heading (**A, B, C, D** or **E**) that is related most closely to the item concerned.

EACH HEADING MAY BE USED ONCE, MORE THAN ONCE OR NOT AT ALL.

Questions 21–24

    A sebaceous gland
    B sweat gland
    C Malpighian layer
    D blood capillaries
    E horny layer

Which of the above skin structures

21 is composed of non-living material?
22 has a duct to the surface of the skin?
23 produces sebum?
24 contains the pigment melanin?

Questions 25–28

    A water
    B urea
    C glucose
    D sodium
    E potassium

Which of the above substances, found in the fluid in Bowman's capsule

25 is not reabsorbed at all?
26 is completely reabsorbed?
27 is a waste product formed by deamination of amino acids?
28 gives an indication of diabetes, if found in the urine?

Questions 29–32

    A water
    B carbon dioxide
    C urea
    D salts
    E faeces

Which of the above

29 is not an excretory product?
30 is excreted only by the lungs?
31 is the major component of urine?
32 is excreted by the kidneys, skin and lungs?

Assertion/Reason

Each of the following questions consists of an *assertion* and a *reason*. Consider both statements and then choose the letter **A, B, C, D** or **E** as your answer according to the following

    A —if both statements are true, and the reason is a correct explanation of the assertion

    B —if both statements are true, but the reason is not a correct explanation of the assertion

    C —if the assertion is true, but the reason is false

    D —if the assertion is false, but the reason is true

    E —if both statements are false.

Code Summarized

	ASSERTION	REASON	
A	true	true	reason is a correct explanation
B	true	true	reason is not a correct explanation
C	true	false	
D	false	true	
E	false	false	

	ASSERTION		REASON
33	Drinking a quantity of salty water will result in the production of more urine	*because*	the kidney excretes more water in order to maintain the salt concentration of the blood.
34	Glucose does not normally appear in the urine	*because*	glucose is not filtered into the nephron.
35	Evaporation of sweat cools the body	*because*	sweat contains water.
36	In very cold conditions frostbite may develop	*because*	the blood supply to the skin is shut off to prevent heat loss.
37	Kidney transplant recipients are liable to secondary infections	*because*	drugs which lower the body's resistance are used to prevent rejection of the kidney after transplantation.

Structured Questions

38   Write short notes on each of the following

    a) the effect of increased body temperature on the skin capillaries

    b) the function of melanin

    c) heatstroke

    d) the effect of a hot, humid atmosphere on the body

    e) the necessity to take salt tablets if working in a hot climate.

39 Explain and give the reason for the effect of four of the following on either the quantity or quality of the urine.

    a) drinking a large amount of water
    b) a lack of insulin from the pancreas
    c) a malfunction of the pituitary gland
    d) eating a meal with a very high protein content
    e) eating a very salty meal.

40

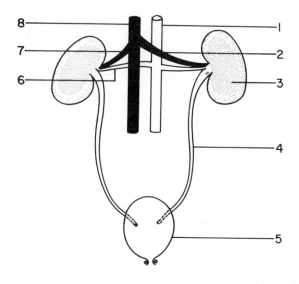

Fig. 23

    a) Name the structures numbered 1–8 in Fig. 23
    b) Give one function of 2, 3, 4, 5 and 6.
    c) Draw a labelled diagram to show the structure of a kidney cut in two vertically.

41 a) Define the term excretion
    b) Name 5 substances excreted by the body and for each one name the excretory organ.
    c) Explain how urine is formed within the kidney.

42 Examine the diagram of the kidney tubule shown in Fig. 24

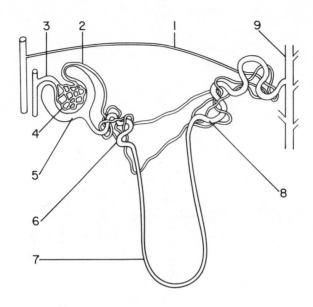

Fig. 24

a) Name the parts numbered 1–9 in Fig. 24
b) Draw an arrow to show the direction of blood flow in the part numbered 1.
c) Write a G on the diagram to indicate the part where glucose is reabsorbed.
d) Write a W on the diagram to indicate the part where most water is reabsorbed.
e) Give three functions of the kidneys.
f) Explain what happens to the following substances, filtered from the blood, as they pass along the tubule

   (i) urea
   (ii) amino acids
   (iii) sodium salts

g) Give the number of the part of the diagram which leads to the ureter.
h) What is the name of the substance which passes down the ureter?

43 Examine the diagram of a vertical section of the skin shown in Fig. 25.

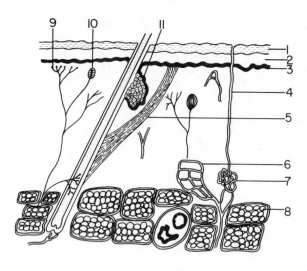

Fig. 25

a) Name the structures numbered 1—11.
b) What is the function of the structure numbered 3?
c) What substance is produced by the structure numbered 11?
d) What is the function of this substance?
e) Explain the part played by the structures numbered 6, 7 and 8 in the regulation of body temperature.

7. The Skeleton, Muscles and Movement

Multiple Choice

In each of the following questions choose *one* only of the letters **A, B, C, D** or **E** to indicate your answer.

1   A large flat bone which forms part of the pectoral girdle is the

   A clavicle
   B scapula
   C femur
   D ulna
   E fibula.

2   The ribs are attached at the front of the skeleton to the

   A humerus
   B scapula
   C clavicle
   D sternum
   E femur.

3   The first vertebra of the human vertebral column is

   A a thoracic vertebra
   B a lumbar vertebra
   C a sacral vertebra
   D the atlas
   E the axis.

4   In which of the following parts of the skeleton would you find a fused joint?

   A skull
   B knee
   C elbow
   D shoulder
   E hip.

5   The neural canal is

   A a canal in the centre of a long bone such as the femur
   B found in the skull
   C a small space between the bones of the wrist
   D a connecting channel between the middle ear and the throat
   E a space in a vertebra through which the spinal cord passes.

Fig. 26 shows some of the bones of the human skeleton. Study this diagram and then answer questions 6-9.

6   The bone numbered 2 is the

    A femur
    B humerus
    C tibia
    D fibula
    E ulna.

7   The part of bone 2 numbered 1 articulates with the

    A pelvic girdle
    B pectoral girdle
    C clavicle
    D metacarpals
    E metatarsals.

8   The joint numbered 3 is a

    A ball and socket joint
    B fixed joint
    C hinge joint
    D sliding joint
    E pivot joint.

9   The bone numbered 4 is the

    A ulna
    B radius
    C tibia
    D fibula
    E femur.

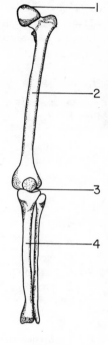

Fig. 26

Fig. 27 shows a typical lumbar vertebra. Study this diagram and then answer questions 10 and 11.

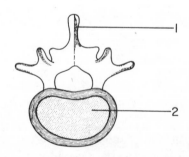

Fig. 27

10 The part numbered 1 in Fig. 27 is the

   A neural arch
   B centrum
   C neural spine
   D neural canal
   E postzygapophysis.

11 The part numbered 2 in Fig. 27 is the

   A centrum
   B neural arch
   C transverse process
   D neural spine
   E disc of cartilage.

12 The principal inorganic component of bone is

   A calcium phosphate
   B magnesium phosphate
   C calcium chloride
   D calcium carbonate
   E magnesium carbonate.

13 Which of the following parts of the skeleton does *not* protect an internal organ?

   A skull
   B vertebral column
   C ribs
   D sternum
   E phalanges.

14 Human bones have all the following functions *except*

   A protection of internal organs
   B sites for attachment of muscles
   C production of red blood cells
   D support of the body
   E storage of glycogen.

15 Muscles are attached to bones by

   A cartilage
   B tendons
   C ligaments
   D a capsule
   E processes.

16 Cardiac muscle is found in the

   A skin
   B heart
   C diaphragm
   D oesophagus
   E upper arm.

17 Which of the following does *not* contain involuntary (smooth or unstriated) muscles?

    A bladder
    B alimentary canal
    C arteries
    D iris diaphragm
    E heart.

Multiple Completion

For each of the following incomplete statements or questions *one* or *more* of the responses numbered 1–4 are correct.

Choose the appropriate letter as your answer according to the following code

    A —if only 1, 2 and 3 are correct
    B —if only 1, 2 and 4 are correct
    C —if only 1 and 4 are correct
    D —if only 3 is correct
    E —if only 2, 3 and 4 are correct.

18 The appendicular skeleton includes the

    1 ulna
    2 skull
    3 ribs
    4 femur.

19 Which of the following are bones of the hand?

    1 phalanges
    2 tarsals
    3 metatarsals
    4 metacarpals.

20 Which of the following is (are) *not* true of the skull?

    1 it has a protective function
    2 the joints between the bones are called sutures
    3 no part of it is moveable
    4 in a young baby all the bones of the skull are not fused.

21 Cartilage can be found

    1 in the oesophagus
    2 in the trachea
    3 between the vertebrae
    4 in the knee joint.

Matching Pairs

Each set of questions consists of five lettered headings **A, B, C, D** and **E** followed by four numbered items. Answer each question by choosing the *one* heading (**A, B, C, D** or **E**) that is related most closely to the item concerned.

EACH HEADING MAY BE USED ONCE, MORE THAN ONCE OR NOT AT ALL.

Questions 22–25

    A patella
    B clavicle
    C scapula
    D fibula
    E tibia.

Which of the above are the correct terms for the

22 shoulderblade?
23 knee cap?
24 collar bone?
25 shin bone?

Questions 26–29

    A ilium, ischium and pubis
    B skull and vertebral column
    C pectoral and pelvic girdles and the limbs
    D clavicle and scapula
    E thoracic vertebrae and ribcage.

Which of the above forms

26 part of the pelvic girdle?
27 the axial skeleton?
28 the complete appendicular skeleton?
29 the pectoral girdle?

Questions 30–33

Which of the following pairs of bones

    A femur and pelvis
    B tarsals and metatarsals
    C atlas and axis
    D metacarpals and phalanges
    E humerus and ulna

forms a

30 hinge joint?
31 ball and socket joint?
32 pivot joint?
33 gliding joint?

Assertion/Reason

Each of the following questions consists of an *assertion* and a *reason*. Consider both statements and then choose the letter **A, B, C, D** or **E** as your answer according to the following

  A —if both statements are true, and the reason is a correct explanation of the assertion
  B —if both statements are true, but the reason is not a correct explanation of the assertion
  C —if the assertion is true, but the reason is false
  D —if the assertion is false, but the reason is true
  E —if both statements are false.

Code Summarized

	ASSERTION	REASON	
A	true	true	reason is a correct explanation
B	true	true	reason is not a correct explanation
C	true	false	
D	false	true	
E	false	false	

	ASSERTION		REASON
34	The foot can move in a circular motion	*because*	there is a ball and socket joint between the bones of the lower leg and the foot.
35	The eighth, ninth and tenth ribs are called floating ribs	*because*	these ribs do not articulate with the sternum.
36	The vertebrae have neural spines	*because*	the neural spines protect the spinal cord.
37	Muscles are found in pairs	*because*	muscles cannot extend.
38	Contraction of smooth muscle is under the control of the will	*because*	smooth muscle has a nerve supply.
39	Sitting slumped in a chair does not cause bad posture	*because*	the muscles compensate for the abnormal position.

40

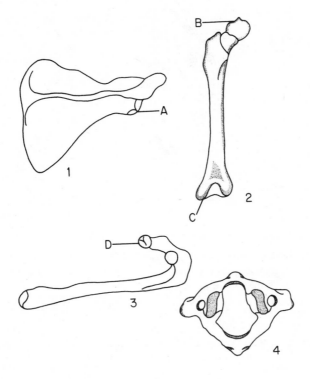

Fig. 28

a) Name each of the bones shown in Fig. 28.

b) Name the bones which articulate with the positions A, B, C and D.

c) Which bone forms part of a girdle?

d) Name the type of joint found at positions A, B and C.

e) Draw a labelled diagram of the bone numbered 2 to show the internal structure as seen in longitudinal section.

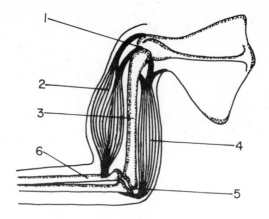

Fig. 29

Fig. 29 shows the bones and muscles of the upper arm.

  a) Name the two joints shown at positions 1 and 5.
  b) Describe the type of movement possible at these two joints.
  c) Name the bones 3 and 6.
  d) The muscles 2 and 4 are an antagonistic pair. Explain the meaning of this term.
  e) Name the muscles 2 and 4.
  f) Draw an arrow on the diagram to indicate the direction in which the lower part of the arm will move when muscle 2 contracts.
  g) If the arm straightened which muscle would relax — 2 or 4?
  h) Name one other position in the body where a joint similar to 1 may be found.

42 a) Draw a clearly labelled diagram of a hinge joint and label the following

  synovial fluid, synovial membrane, cartilage, ligaments and the bones on either side of the joint.

  b) State the function of

  (i) synovial fluid
  (ii) cartilage
  (iii) ligaments.

43 a) Which part of the skeleton is shown in Fig. 30? How do you recognize it as such?
  b) Name the bones numbered 1, 3, 4, 5 and 7.
  c) Two muscles are shown, numbered 2 and 6. Which of the muscles raises the bones 4 and 5 when it contracts?
  d) Which of the muscles extends the bones 4 and 5 when it contracts?
  e) Name the joint labelled X.
  f) What type of movement is possible at this joint?
  g) What type of joint is found between bones 1 and 7?
  h) Which bones are found at the lower end of bones 4 and 5?

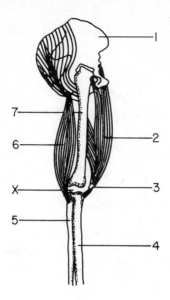

Fig. 30

8. Nervous and Hormonal Co-ordination

Multiple Choice

In each of the following questions choose *one* only of the letters **A, B, C, D** or **E** to indicate your answer.

1 Which of the following statements concerning a reflex action is *incorrect?*

    A it is involuntary
    B it is very rapid
    C it involves both receptor and effector organs
    D it happens without the brain being aware of it
    E it often prevents damage to the body.

2 The largest and most well-developed part of the human brain is the

    A cerebrum
    B cerebellum
    C thalamus
    D medulla oblongata
    E pineal body.

Study Fig. 31 and then answer questions 3–5.

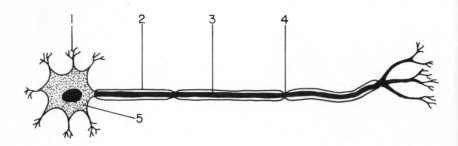

Fig. 31

3 The axon is numbered

    A 1
    B 2
    C 3
    D 4
    E 5.

4   The dendrites are numbered

    A 1
    B 2
    C 3
    D 4
    E 5.

5   A synapse is

    A the structure numbered 4
    B a special term given to the nucleus of the cell
    C the part of the axon which transmits nerve impulses
    D the structure numbered 2
    E a microscopic gap that separates one neuron from another.

6   When sound waves enter the ear the first part to vibrate is the

    A oval window
    B incus
    C malleus
    D fluid in the cochlea
    E tympanic membrane.

7   The part of the ear responsible for maintaining an equal pressure on either side of the eardrum is the

    A ear ossicles
    B cochlea
    C semi-circular canals
    D external auditory meatus
    E eustachian tube.

8   Which eye defect causes light rays to be focused in front of the retina?

    A astigmatism
    B oldsight or presbyopia
    C short sight or myopia
    D long sight or hypermetropia
    E conjunctivitis.

9   The front of the tongue is sensitive to

    A bitter sensations only
    B sweet and salt sensations
    C sour and sweet sensations
    D bitter and sour sensations
    E bitter and salt sensations.

10   The fovea of the eye contains

    A no rods or cones
    B cones only
    C rods only
    D rods and cones in equal numbers
    E twice as many cones as rods.

11 The semi-circular canals of the ear are responsible for the sense of

    A balance
    B hearing
    C taste
    D pain
    E pressure.

12 Which of the following is *not* solely an endocrine gland?

    A thyroid
    B adrenal
    C pituitary
    D pancreas
    E thymus.

13 Which of the following glands secretes the hormone which prepares the body for 'fight or flight'?

    A pituitary
    B pancreas
    C adrenal
    D thyroid
    E thymus.

14 Undersecretion of the hormone from the thyroid gland in an adult causes

    A glucose to be excreted in the urine
    B protrusion of the eyeballs
    C slow speech, baldness and dry, thickened skin
    D dwarfism but normal mental development
    E gigantism.

15 Which of the following is *not* a correct statement concerning hormones?

    A they are produced by ductless glands
    B they are transported in the blood
    C they are chemicals
    D they affect other organs in the body
    E no hormone is produced which affects the kidney.

Multiple Completion

For each of the following incomplete statements or questions *one* or *more* of the responses numbered 1–4 are correct.

Choose the appropriate letter as your answer according to the following code

    A —if only 1, 2 and 3 are correct
    B —if only 1, 2 and 4 are correct
    C —if only 1 and 4 are correct
    D —if only 3 is correct
    E —if only 2, 3 and 4 are correct.

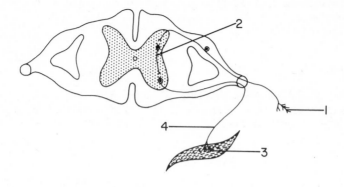

Fig. 32

Fig. 32 represents a reflex arc such as in the knee-jerk reflex. Which of the following statements is (are) true of such a reflex?

1 the stimulus is picked up by the structure numbered 1
2 the impulses pass from 1 to 2 to 3
3 the brain is unaware of the response
4 the structure numbered 4 is a motor neuron.

17 Accommodation of the eye for distance vision is brought about by

1 relaxation of ciliary muscles
2 contraction of suspensory ligaments
3 contraction of circular muscles of iris
4 flattening of the lens.

18 Long sightedness may be caused by

1 a thin, weak lens
2 an eyeball which is too short
3 a hardened lens
4 a deformed cornea.

19 It is true to say of the cochlea that it

1 can be damaged by prolonged exposure to very loud noise
2 is connected to the auditory nerve
3 is concerned with the sense of balance
4 contains a fluid.

20 The pituitary gland secretes

1 adrenalin
2 thyroxine
3 prolactin
4 insulin.

21 An under-active thyroid gland can result in

    1 cretinism
    2 failure of development of secondary sexual characteristics
    3 goitre
    4 lethargy and baldness.

Matching Pairs

Each set of questions consists of five lettered headings **A, B, C, D** and **E** followed by four numbered items. Answer each question by choosing the *one* heading (**A, B, C, D** or **E**) that is related most closely to the item concerned.

EACH HEADING MAY BE USED ONCE, MORE THAN ONCE OR NOT AT ALL.

Questions 22–25

    A medulla oblongata
    B cerebellum
    C cerebral hemispheres
    D pituitary
    E thalamus

Which of the above parts of the brain

22 receives impulses from sensory receptors?
23 controls the body temperature?
24 produces hormones?
25 maintains balance and posture?

Questions 26–29

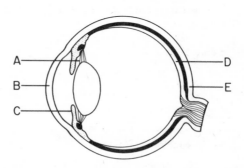

Fig. 33

Which of the above parts of the eye shown in Fig. 33

26 is attached to the lens?
27 contains both radial and circular muscles?
28 contains rods and cones?
29 is a transparent layer?

Questions 30–33

Refer again to Fig. 33. Which of the lettered structures

30 is sensitive to light?
31 may be replaced by a surgical graft?
32 controls the size of the pupil?
33 is the sclerotic layer?

Questions 34–37

Which of the following stimuli

    A temperature
    B salt
    C pain
    D pressure within tissues
    E touch

is detected by

34 Meissner's corpuscles?
35 Pacinian corpuscles?
36 free nerve endings?
37 taste buds?

Assertion/Reason

Each of the following questions consists of an *assertion* and a *reason*. Consider both statements and then choose the letter **A, B, C, D** or **E** as your answer according to the following

    A —if both statements are true, and the reason is a correct explanation of the assertion
    B —if both statements are true, but the reason is not a correct explanation of the assertion
    C —if the assertion is true, but the reason is false
    D —if the assertion is false, but the reason is true
    E —if both statements are false.

Code Summarized

	ASSERTION	REASON	
A	true	true	reason is a correct explanation
B	true	true	reason is not a correct explanation
C	true	false	
D	false	true	
E	false	false	

	ASSERTION		REASON
38	Swallowing is not a reflex action	*because*	the swallowing response needs to be learnt after birth.
39	The eye is able to perceive colours	*because*	the retina contains rods.

40	Longsightedness may be cured by wearing spectacles with convex lenses	*because*	convex lenses cause the light rays to converge.
41	A person with astigmatism cannot focus simultaneously on lines at right angles to each other	*because*	the cornea is deformed.
42	Perceptual deafness may be helped by hearing aids	*because*	the hearing aid amplifies the sound waves.
43	Diabetics need to have daily injections of insulin	*because*	insulin cannot be taken by mouth since it is a protein.

Structured Questions

44

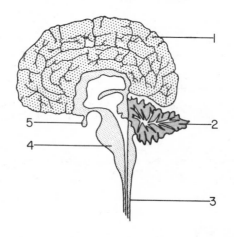

Fig. 34

a) Match the following to the numbered structures in Fig. 34

   (i) Pituitary gland
   (ii) Spinal cord
   (iii) Cerebral hemisphere
   (iv) Cerebellum
   (v) Medulla oblongata

b) Name the part of Fig. 34 which

    (i) controls the movements of the eyes
    (ii) receives impulses from the eyes
    (iii) controls the muscles maintaining balance
    (iv) produces hormones
    (v) is protected by vertebrae

c) Write the names of the following structures involved in a reflex arc in the correct order
Motor neurone, sensory neurone, receptor, effector, intermediate neurone.

45 a) Draw a diagram of a vertical section through the human eye and label the following

       conjunctiva, choroid, sclerotic, iris, pupil, lens, suspensory ligaments, retina, fovea, optic nerve, ciliary muscles, cornea, blind spot.

b) Give one function of each of the following

    (i) lens
    (ii) retina
    (iii) ciliary muscle
    (iv) optic nerve.

c) Describe the changes that take place in the eye when a person looks up from reading a book to stare at a plane in the sky.

46 a) Explain, by using labelled diagrams, the meaning of long and short sight.
b) Explain how these eye defects may be corrected.
c) Explain how sound waves entering the ear are transmitted to the brain.

47 a) Describe the response of the pupil of the eye when

    (i) a person enters a dark cinema
    (ii) a bright light is shone into the eye.

b) Explain how the responses in (a) above are brought about.

c) Explain the meaning of the terms

    (i) blind spot
    (ii) fovea
    (iii) vitreous humour.

48

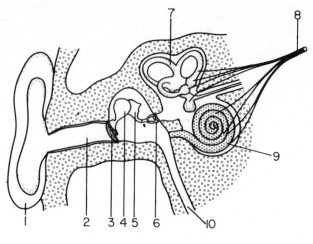

Fig. 35

a) Name the parts numbered 1–10 in Fig. 35
b) State one function of the parts numbered 2, 3, 6, 7, 8 and 10.
c) What are the possible causes of temporary deafness associated with the parts numbered 2 and 10.
d) In a child who is born totally deaf, which numbered structure is likely to be non-functional?

49

GLAND	HORMONE	FUNCTION
PITUITARY		
THYROID		
ADRENAL		
OVARY		
PANCREAS		
TESTIS		

Complete the table above by writing the *number* of a hormone from List A next to the gland which produces that hormone.

In the same way choose a function from List B and write the *number* of that function to the correct hormone.

List A

1 insulin
2 testosterone
3 thyroxine
4 prolactin
5 adrenalin
6 progesterone

List B

7 stimulates milk secretion
8 regulates growth rate
9 regulates blood sugar level
10 prepares body for pregnancy
11 stimulates secondary sexual characteristics
12 controls pulse and respiratory rate

9. Growth and Reproduction

Multiple Choice

In each of the following questions choose *one* only of the letters **A, B, C, D** or **E** to indicate your answer.

Refer to Fig. 36 and then answer questions 1–4.

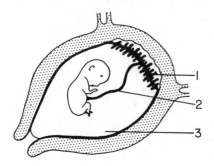

Fig. 36

1 The space numbered 3 in Fig. 36 contains

    A amniotic fluid
    B aqueous humour
    C synovial fluid
    D air
    E tissue fluid.

2 Which of the following is *not* true of the structure numbered 1?

    A it allows respiratory gases to pass to the foetus
    B it carries excretory products from the foetus
    C it allows glucose and amino acids to pass to the foetus
    D it develops from the chorion
    E it completes the circulatory exchange of maternal blood and foetal blood.

3 The structure numbered 2 is the

    A placenta
    B amnion
    C chorion
    D oviduct
    E umbilical cord.

4 The age of the foetus shown in Fig. 36 is approximately

    A 4 weeks
    B 2 months
    C 8 months
    D 6 months
    E 4 months.

Refer to Fig. 37 and then answer questions 5–7.

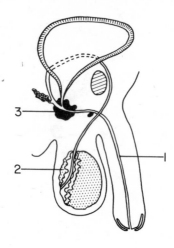

Fig. 37

5 The structure numbered 1 is the

    A epididymis
    B seminiferous tubule
    C ureter
    D urethra
    E vas deferens.

6 The number of chromosomes present in the cells produced by the structure numbered 2 is

    A 46
    B 23
    C 18
    D 12
    E 6.

7 The structure numbered 3 is the

    A seminal vesicle
    B testis
    C vas deferens
    D bladder
    E prostate gland.

8 Fertilization normally occurs in the

    A ovary
    B uterus
    C cervix
    D vagina
    E fallopian tube.

9 The gestation period is defined as

    A the time taken for a fertilized egg to implant in the uterus
    B the time taken for the actual birth to take place
    C the time taken for the sperm to find and fertilize the egg
    D the period of time between fertilization and birth
    E the period of time between birth and the development of secondary sexual characteristics.

10 The corpus luteum develops from

    A the oviduct
    B a Graafian follicle
    C an ovum
    D the ovary
    E an oogonium.

11 The process of fusion of an egg and a sperm is termed

    A mitosis
    B implantation
    C meiosis
    D parturition
    E fertilization.

12 The hormone which stimulates egg production is called

    A progesterone
    B luteinizing hormone
    C follicle-stimulating hormone
    D oestrogen
    E testosterone.

13 After the birth of a baby, the mother produces the hormone prolactin. The effect of this is to

    A stimulate milk production
    B prevent further contractions of the uterus
    C prevent lactation
    D cause ovulation to restart
    E cause repair to the lining of the uterus.

14 Ovulation normally occurs

    A during menstruation
    B only when an egg has been fertilized
    C as a result of sexual intercourse
    D approximately 14 days before menstruation
    E only up to the age of 25.

15 Growth in height stops

    A at puberty
    B at age 16
    C when the menopause is reached
    D when the thyroid gland ceases to secrete hormones
    E when ossification is complete.

Multiple Completion

For each of the following incomplete statements or questions *one* or *more* of the responses numbered 1–4 are correct.

Choose the appropriate letter as your answer according to the following code

    A —if only 1, 2 and 3 are correct
    B —if only 1, 2 and 4 are correct
    C —if only 1 and 4 are correct
    D —if only 3 is correct
    E —if only 2, 3 and 4 are correct.

16 The placenta

    1 contains foetal and maternal blood vessels
    2 acts as an endocrine organ
    3 completely surrounds the foetus
    4 is connected to the umbilical cord.

17 Through which of the following structures do sperm pass in moving from the testes to the outside?

    1 epididymis
    2 ureter
    3 scrotum
    4 urethra.

18 Through which of the following structures does an unfertilized egg pass?

    1 vagina
    2 uterus
    3 urethra
    4 fallopian tube.

19   Which of the following is (are) indications that birth is about to take place?

    1   frequent, periodic contractions of the uterus
    2   breaking of the umbilical cord
    3   hearing the baby's heart beat
    4   'breaking of the waters'.

20   The ovary

    1   becomes active between the ages of 11 and 14
    2   contains blood vessels, eggs and corpus lutea
    3   is the site of fertilization
    4   produces hormones.

21   The testes

    1   have a slightly lower temperature than the rest of the body
    2   produce cells of the same size as eggs
    3   are protected by the pelvic girdle
    4   are the site of meiosis in the male.

Matching Pairs

Each set of questions consists of five lettered headings **A, B, C, D** and **E** followed by four numbered items. Answer each question by choosing the *one* heading (**A, B, C, D** or **E**) that is related most closely to the item concerned.

EACH HEADING MAY BE USED ONCE, MORE THAN ONCE OR NOT AT ALL.

Questions 22–25

    A testes
    B placenta
    C uterus
    D pituitary gland
    E seminal vesicle

Which of the above structures

  22 secretes a hormone stimulating milk production?
  23 produces testosterone?
  24 is found in the scrotum?
  25 contains the developing foetus?

Questions 26–29

A testes
B urethra
C prostate gland
D vas deferens
E bladder

Which of the above structures

26 transports both sperm and urine?
27 produces semen?
28 produces sperm?
29 transports sperm only?

Questions 30–33

A ovary
B ovum
C foetus
D umbilical cord
E fertilized ovum

Which of the above

30 is a zygote?
31 is an organ which produces female gametes?
32 becomes implanted in the uterus?
33 connects the embryo to the placenta?

Questions 34–37

A parturition
B ovulation
C fertilization
D menstruation
E micturation

Which of the above

34 refers to the production of an egg from the ovary?
35 refers to the act of giving birth?
36 refers to the penetration of the egg by the sperm and the fusion of the nuclei?
37 occurs approximately 14 days after the start of menstruation?

Assertion/Reason

Each of the following questions consists of an *assertion* and a *reason*. Consider both statements and then choose the letter **A, B, C, D** or **E** as your answer according to the following

A —if both statements are true, and the reason is a correct explanation of the assertion

B —if both statements are true, but the reason is not a correct explanation of the assertion

C —if the assertion is true, but the reason is false

D —if the assertion is false, but the reason is true

E —if both statements are false.

Code Summarized

	ASSERTION	REASON	
A	true	true	reason is a correct explanation
B	true	true	reason is not a correct explanation
C	true	false	
D	false	true	
E	false	false	

	ASSERTION		REASON
38	The testes lie outside the abdominal cavity	*because*	the lower temperature is more favourable to sperm production.
39	The developing embryo is protected in the uterus	*because*	the embryo is surrounded by amniotic fluid.
40	When the fertilized egg reaches the uterus it consists of a cluster of cells	*because*	immediately after fertilization the egg undergoes mitosis.
41	The embryo receives its supply of oxygen from the mother	*because*	the maternal and foetal blood mix.
42	Twins may be conceived from the fertilization of one egg	*because*	two sperms may fertilize the egg.
43	A vasectomy prevents conception	*because*	the oviducts are tied.

44

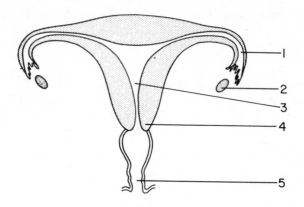

Fig. 38

a) Name the structures numbered 1–5 in Fig. 38.

b) Give the number *only* of the structure

    (i) in which ovulation occurs
    (ii) which receives sperm from the male
    (iii) in which fertilization occurs
    (iv) in which implantation occurs
    (v) which sheds part of its wall during menstruation.

c) Mark on the diagram

    (i) with arrows, the path of the egg if it is not fertilized
    (ii) with an M, the place where a mucus plug is formed during pregnancy
    (iii) with a P, the position of the placenta during pregnancy.

45 Consider the following information

    (i) an egg is released once during a menstrual cycle
    (ii) ovulation is accompanied by a rise in temperature
    (iii) the egg lives for approximately 24 hours
    (iv) sperms can survive for approximately 2–3 days in the female reproductive tract.

Now examine Fig. 39 and answer the questions.

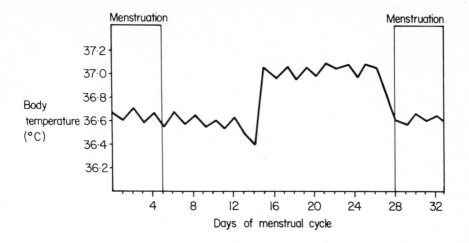

Fig. 39

a) On which day does ovulation occur? Explain your answer.

b) What is the normal body temperature for this subject?

c) During which days of the cycle is normal body temperature maintained?

d) Name the method of contraception which relies largely on the information shown in Fig. 39.

e) Give two reasons why this is not a very successful method of contraception.

f) During which of the following days would intercourse provide the best chance of conception?
   (i) 9–11
   (ii) 13–15
   (iii) 20–22

g) If a couple did not wish to conceive, when during the cycle would it be safe to have intercourse without use of any other contraceptive method?

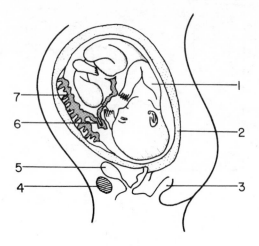

Fig. 40

a) Name the structures numbered 1–7 in Fig. 40.
b) State two functions of the structure numbered 2.
c) State two functions of the structure numbered 7.
d) State one function of the structure numbered 6.
e) What stage in pregnancy does the diagram represent?
f) What causes birth of the baby?
g) Name one mineral required by the foetus for the production of its red blood cells.

47 From the list below choose the structure which carries out the functions shown in the table and write the name of the structure in the table.

LIST
OVARY, UTERUS, FALLOPIAN TUBE, TESTES, MAMMARY GLAND, UMBILICAL CORD, PITUITARY GLAND, URETHRA, URETER, PLACENTA.

FUNCTION	STRUCTURE
Contracts at birth	
Produces eggs	
Produces sperms	
A structure in which fertilization occurs	
Connects the embryo to the placenta	
Produces milk	
Produces oxytocin	
Carries both sperm and urine	
Carries urine only	
Allows the foetus to obtain food and oxygen	

48

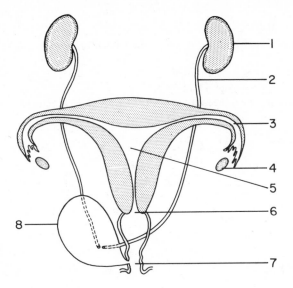

Fig. 41

a) Name the structures numbered 1–8 in Fig. 41.

b) Give the number *only* of the structure which

   (i) produces eggs
   (ii) stores urine
   (iii) produces urine
   (iv) produces hormones
   (v) holds the foetus during pregnancy
   (vi) contains amniotic fluid during pregnancy.

c) Give the numbers of the parts, in their correct sequence, through which sperm pass in order to fertilize the egg.

d) Which structure is not shown in its true position on the diagram?

49 a) How many chromosomes are present in the nuclei of eggs and sperm? Name the process of nuclear division which halves the number of chromosomes when eggs are formed.

b) How many chromosomes are present in a fertilized egg?

c) Name the process of nuclear division which takes place when a fertilized egg divides.

d) What is the significance of the difference in the number of chromosomes between a fertilized egg and an unfertilized egg?

e) The table below shows the average weight of a developing foetus from 3 months to birth.

AGE (months)	WEIGHT (grams)	INCREASE IN WEIGHT (grams)
3	50	—
4	150	
5	300	
6	650	
7	1200	
8	1700	
9	2250	
Birth	3250	

(i) Complete the table to show the increase in weight per month.

(ii) Plot a graph of the weight of the foetus from 3 months to birth.

(iii) Between which two months did the foetus put on the most weight?

(iv) Between which two months did the foetus put on the least weight?

(v) Which month showed the greatest *percentage* increase in weight?

(vi) At the end of 8 months the foetus has developed all its necessary organs. Explain why the graph continues to rise after this time?

10. Inheritance and Populations

In each of the following questions choose *one* only of the letters **A, B, C, D** or **E** to indicate your answer.

1   The person referred to as the 'Father of Genetics' was

   A Pasteur
   B Darwin
   C Mendel
   D Fleming
   E Malthus.

2   Which of the following organisms was first used in genetic studies?

   A fruit flies
   B mice
   C tomato plants
   D pea plants
   E flour beetles.

3   DNA is found mainly in the

   A mitochondria
   B cell membrane
   C ribosomes
   D vacuole
   E nucleus.

4   The number of chromosomes in a human sperm is

   A 6
   B 12
   C 23
   D 46
   E 8.

5   The term used to describe a new characteristic which appears suddenly due to a change in the genetic material is

   A genotype
   B hybrid
   C recessive allele
   D phenotype
   E mutation.

6 The number of chromosomes in a body cell is

    A 6
    B 12
    C 23
    D 46
    E 52.

7 Which of the following is *not* entirely a genetically-controlled characteristic?

    A intelligence
    B blood group
    C tongue-rolling
    D ability to taste PTC (phenylthiocarbamide)
    E hair colour.

8 A dominant gene is represented by T and the recessive gene by t. If the offspring of a cross gave a ratio of 1Tt to 1tt the genotypes of the parents would be

    A TT × tt
    B Tt × tt
    C TT × Tt
    D TT × TT
    E Tt × Tt.

In man 'blue eyes' is recessive to 'brown eyes'. Use this information in items 9, 10, 11 and 12.

9 A brown-eyed man marries a blue-eyed woman. Which of the following statements is the most accurate concerning the children of that marriage?

    A all the children will have brown eyes
    B all the children will have blue eyes
    C half will have blue eyes and half brown
    D three-quarters of the children will be blue-eyed
    E any blue-eyed children will be homozygous.

10 Two people heterozygous for brown eyes marry. They have four children of the genotypes BB, Bb, Bb and bb. How many of the children have brown eyes?

    A 1
    B 2
    C 3
    D 4
    E none.

11 How many of the children in question 10 above are homozygous for brown eyes?

    A 1
    B 2
    C 3
    D 4
    E none.

12 A man homozygous for brown eye colour marries a woman homozygous for blue eyes. They have 1 child. Which of the following correctly describes the child's genotype and phenotype?

    A genotype — BB, phenotype — brown eyes
    B genotype — Bb, phenotype — blue eyes
    C genotype — Bb, phenotype — brown eyes
    D genotype — bb, phenotype — brown eyes
    E genotype — bb, phenotype — blue eyes.

In man, 'curly hair' is dominant to 'straight hair'. Use this information in items 13 and 14.

13 A man heterozygous for curly hair marries a straight-haired woman. The expected ratio of their children with regard to curly and straight hair would be

    A 1 : 1
    B 3 : 1
    C 2 : 1
    D all curly
    E all straight.

14 If 2 people heterozygous for curly hair marry and have children it is likely that

    A all the children will be homozygous
    B all the children will be heterozygous
    C all the children will have the same genotype
    D all the children will have curly hair
    E some of the children will have straight hair.

15 Which statement is *incorrect* concerning the inheritance of blood groups?

    A a person of blood group O has the genotype OO
    B gene O is recessive to gene A
    C a person of blood group B has the genotype BB or BO
    D gene O is recessive to gene B
    E gene A is recessive to gene B.

16 Which region has the lowest death rate?

    A India
    B Africa
    C Asia
    D South America
    E Europe.

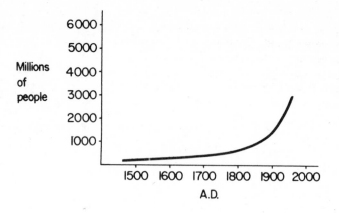

Fig. 42

Examine Fig. 42 which shows the world's population increase from the year 1500 to the present. What is the world's population likely to be in the year 2000?

  A 3800 million
  B 4200 million
  C 4500 million
  D 5000 million
  E 5500 million

Multiple Completion

For each of the following incomplete statements or questions *one* or *more* of the responses numbered 1–4 are correct.

Choose the appropriate letter as your answer according to the following code

  A —if only 1, 2 and 3 are correct
  B —if only 1, 2 and 4 are correct
  C —if only 1 and 4 are correct
  D —if only 3 is correct
  E —if only 2, 3 and 4 are correct.

18 Examples of discontinuous variation are

  1 ABO blood groups
  2 height
  3 weight
  4 tongue-rolling.

19 Genetic studies of the type carried out on animals cannot be done on man. Which of the following have contributed to our knowledge of human genetics?

    1 study of family pedigrees
    2 study of identical twins
    3 statistical analyses of large numbers of individuals
    4 use of the back-cross.

20 It is true to say of identical twins that they

    1 have the same genetic constitution
    2 are of the same sex
    3 resemble each other more closely than non-identical twins
    4 result from the fertilization of two eggs.

21 Fig. 43 represents a marriage between a curly-haired man and a straight-haired woman (curly [C] dominant to straight [c]).

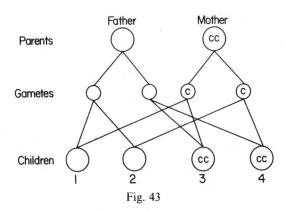

Fig. 43

It is true to say of this family that

    1 the genotype of the father is Cc
    2 child number 1 has straight hair
    3 child number 3 has curly hair
    4 the genotype of child number 2 is Cc.

22 A man of blood group A marries a woman of blood group B and they have 4 children. Which of the following is (are) true of this family?

    1 The father's genotype may be AO.
    2 One of the children may be blood group O.
    3 None of the children could be blood group AB.
    4 One of the children may be blood group A.

23 Which of the following is (are) true of the human population?

    1 Britain has a higher birth rate than India.
    2 Disease and famine are checks to population growth.
    3 In Britain life expectancy has risen in the last 100 years.
    4 The infant mortality rate in Britain is less than in Pakistan.

24 Which of the following is (are) factors which tend to increase the world's population?

    1 new methods of food production
    2 educating people to use contraceptives
    3 natural disasters such as earthquakes and famine
    4 establishing a welfare state.

25 Fig. 44 shows the frequency of family size in small sample of families.

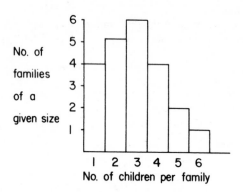

Fig. 44

Which of the statements on this information is (are) true?

    1 The number of families in the sample is 22.
    2 The mean family size is 3.4.
    3 Three of the families in the sample have 4 children.
    4 The total number of children is 64.

Matching Pairs

Each set of questions consists of five lettered headings **A, B, C, D** and **E** followed by four numbered items. Answer each question by choosing the *one* heading (**A, B, C, D** or **E**) that is related most closely to the item concerned.

EACH HEADING MAY BE USED ONCE, MORE THAN ONCE OR NOT AT ALL.

Questions 26–29

    A mutation
    B genotype
    C phenotype
    D gene
    E genetics

Match the terms above to the following definitions.

26 a spontaneous change in a gene or chromosome

27 the genetic constitution of an organism

28 the observable characteristics of an organism

29 the study of inheritance.

Questions 30–33

    A sickle-cell anaemia

    B haemophilia

    C mongolism

    D brachydactyly

    E red hair colour

Which of the above is

30 caused by an incompletely dominant gene?

31 caused by an extra chromosome?

32 caused by a dominant gene?

33 a sex-linked disease?

Questions 34–37

Achondroplastic dwarfism is a genetic defect caused by a dominant gene. Fig. 45 shows a family pedigree for this defect.

Let D represent the dominant allele and d the recessive allele.

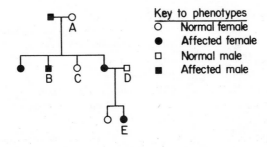

Fig. 45

Which of the people A–E in Fig. 45.

34 is a male with the genotype dd?

35 is the grandmother of E?

36 is a normal female in the first generation?

37 is a male in the first generation with a genotype of Dd?

Questions 38-41

A crude birth rate
B crude death rate
C mortality rate
D contraception
E fertility rate

Which of the above

38 is a method of reducing the birth rate?
39 is defined as the number of deaths from a disease per 1000 of the population?
40 is likely to be high in a population with a large proportion of young women?
41 is defined as the number of live births per 1000 of the population per year?

Assertion/Reason

Each of the following questions consists of an *assertion* and a *reason*. Consider both statements and then choose the letter **A, B, C, D** or **E** as your answer according to the following.

    A —if both statements are true, and the reason is a correct explanation of the assertion

    B —if both statements are true, but the reason is not a correct explanation of the assertion

    C —if the assertion is true, but the reason is false

    D —if the assertion is false, but the reason is true

    E —if both statements are false.

Code Summarized

	ASSERTION	REASON	
A	true	true	reason is a correct explanation
B	true	true	reason is not a correct explanation
C	true	false	
D	false	true	
E	false	false	

	ASSERTION		REASON
42	Cells produced by meiosis have 23 chromosomes	*because*	the chromosome number is halved during meiosis.
43	Identical twins are always of the same sex and look alike	*because*	identical twins share the same placenta.
44	Down's syndrome is a mental deficiency	*because*	the condition arises as a chromosome mutation.
45	Haemophilia is more common in females	*because*	the gene responsible for haemophilia is found on the Y chromosome.

46	The ratio of boys to girls is approximately 1 : 1	*because*	there is an equal chance of sperm carrying an X or Y chromosome fertilising an egg.
47	The world's population has risen rapidly in the last 100 years	*because*	many previously fatal diseases can now be cured.

Structured Questions

48 a) In man brown hair (B) is dominant to red (b). If a man with brown hair married a woman with red hair what colour hair would their children have if

    (i) the man was homozymous for brown hair
    (ii) the man was heterozyous for brown hair.

  b) Explain the difference between

    (i) homozygous and heterozygous
    (ii) genotype and phenotype
    (iii) dominant and recessive characteristics.

49 a) Brown eye colour is dominant to blue. In the family represented in Fig 46, the mother and two daughters have blue eyes and John has brown eyes. Using the symbols, B for brown eyes and b for blue eyes complete the genetic make-up of the family shown in Fig. 46.

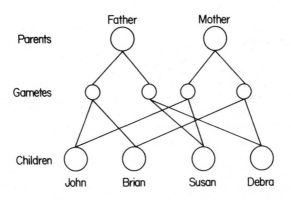

Fig. 46

  b) What eye colour do the father and Brian have? Explain how you arrived at your answer.
  c) If John marries a girl with blue eyes what eye colour are their children likely to have?

50 In man albinism (absence of pigment from skin, hair and eyes) is caused by a recessive gene — a. The normal condition can be represented by the symbol — A.

a) Indicate, on Fig. 47, the genotype of each individual.

(There are no albinos in the F_1 generation)

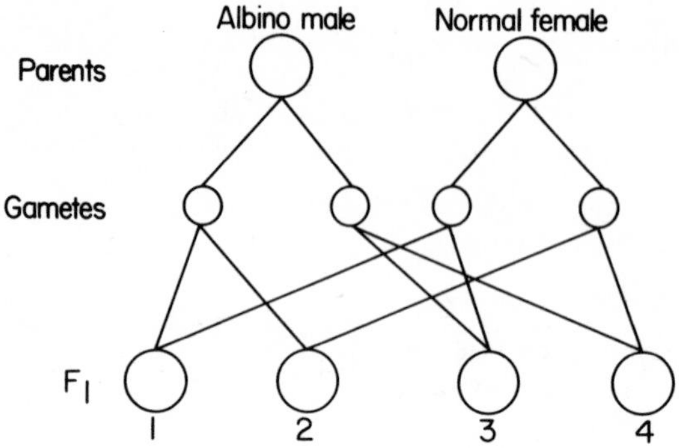

Fig. 47

b) Prepare a similar diagram to show the genotypes and phenotypes of the parents and children of a marriage between number 4 in (a) above and a person of the same genotype.

c) Prepare a diagram to show the genotypes and phenotypes of the parents and children of a marriage between number 1 in (a) above and an albino.

51 Haemophilia (the inability of the blood to clot) is caused by a sex-linked recessive gene.

Draw diagrams to illustrate the genotypes and phenotypes of the parents and children of the following marriages, each of which produces four children.

(Use the symbol H for the normal condition and h for the haemophiliac condition)

a) A haemophiliac man and a normal (non-carrier) woman.

b) A normal man and a carrier woman.

c) A haemophiliac man and a carrier woman.

52 Fig. 48 shows a family pedigree for brown and blue eyes. 'Brown eyes' is dominant to 'blue eyes'.

a) What are the genotypes of 1, 5 and 7? Explain how you arrive at your answer.

(Use the symbol B for brown eyes and b for blue eyes)

b) What are the genotypes and phenotypes of 2, 3, 4, 6 and 8? Explain how you arrive at your answer.

c) If the female 9 marries a brown-eyed man and they have four children, explain the possible genotypes and phenotypes of their children.

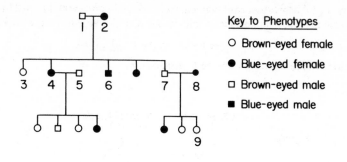

Key to Phenotypes

○ Brown-eyed female

● Blue-eyed female

□ Brown-eyed male

■ Blue-eyed male

Fig. 48

53 Fig. 49 shows a family pedigree for the inheritance of an abnormal trait which is inherited as a recessive—a. AA and Aa individuals are normal, aa individuals show the trait.

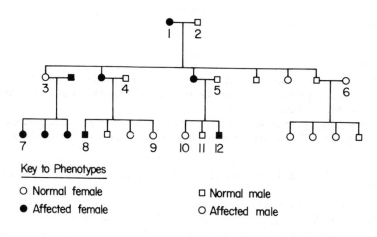

Key to Phenotypes

○ Normal female   □ Normal male

● Affected female   ○ Affected male

Fig. 49

a) What are the genotypes of 1, 2, 3, 4 and 5?

b) Is it possible to state with certainty that 6 has a genotype of AA? Explain your answer.

c) If 7 marries a heterozygous male what proportion of their children are likely to be affected?

d) Work out the proportions of genotypes and phenotypes which could be produced by the following marriages

   (i) 8 × 10

   (ii) 7 × 12

   (iii) 9 × 11

54 Mrs. Smith had a condition called polydactyly (extra digits on the limb) caused by a dominant gene. The woman's father, Mr. Jones also had the condition but Mrs. Jones was normal. Mr. Jones's mother was also normal.

Mrs. Smith marries a normal man and they have four children, John and David, Susan and Angela. The girls are normal but the boys are not.

a) Construct a family pedigree of all the people mentioned. Indicate females with a circle and males with a square. Use blacked-out circles or squares to indicate people with polydactyly.

b) Using the symbol P for polydactyly, p for the normal condition give the genotypes of

   (i) Mrs. Smith
   (ii) Mr. Smith
   (iii) Mr. Jones
   (iv) the four children.

c) Which person, not mentioned above, transmitted this condition to the family? Why is it not possible to state with certainty this person's genotype?

55 Explain the possible effects of each of the following on the population of a country

a) an improved health programme
b) large scale famine
c) increased use of contraception
d) increased agricultural productivity.

11. Microbiology and Disease

Multiple Choice

In each of the following questions choose *one* only of the letters **A, B, C, D** or **E** to indicate your answer.

1 Which of the following is an ectoparasite of man?

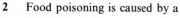

  A *Plasmodium*
  B ringworm
  C *Salmonella*
  D tapeworm
  E *Schistosoma.*

2 Food poisoning is caused by a

  A fungus
  B virus
  C tapeworm
  D bacterium
  E protozoan.

3 A disease which may be caught from a dog bite is

  A typhoid
  B rubella
  C hydrophobia
  D tuberculosis
  E measles.

4 Poliomyelitis is caused by a

  A fungus
  B bacterium
  C virus
  D tapeworm
  E protozoan.

5 All the following are infectious diseases *except*

  A tuberculosis
  B cholera
  C typhoid
  D influenza
  E haemophilia.

6 Which of the following diseases is spread by droplet infection?

    A influenza
    B typhoid
    C malaria
    D syphilis
    E sleeping sickness.

7 BCG vaccine is used to provide protection from

    A smallpox
    B tuberculosis
    C malaria
    D cholera
    E poliomyelitis.

8 The most likely factor leading to the recovery from lung cancer is

    A banning cigarettes
    B immunization
    C use of surgery
    D early diagnosis
    E use of radio-therapy.

9 Which of the following would *not* be detected by mass chest X-ray?

    A lung cancer
    B tuberculosis
    C breast cancer
    D bronchitis
    E cervical cancer

10 A disease is said to be endemic when

    A it is extremely infectious
    B it must be notified to the Health Authorities
    C there is a large outbreak of the disease
    D the disease spreads rapidly from country to country
    E it is always present in a country.

11 The most frequent cause of death in underdeveloped countries is

    A lung cancer
    B heart disease
    C obesity
    D malaria
    E malnutrition.

12 The first person to use carbolic acid (phenol) to kill germs during surgery was

    A Lister
    B Koch
    C Jenner
    D Pasteur
    E Ross.

3 Penicillin was discovered by Alexander Fleming in 1928. When did it come into general use?

    A 1931
    B 1936
    C 1945
    D 1940
    E 1952.

14 If a bacterium divides once every 20 minutes how many would there be after 2 hours?

    A 48
    B 32
    C 256
    D 64
    E 128.

15 An experiment was set up to determine the effect of the antibiotic streptomycin on three species of bacteria. The three bacteria were streaked across a prepared agar plate. A narrow channel was cut out of the agar and a solution of the antibiotic placed in the channel. The plate was then incubated at 37°C for three days. The results are shown in Fig. 50.

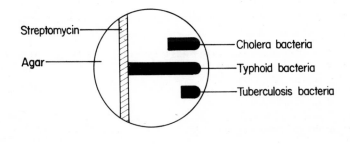

Fig. 50

From the results shown in Fig. 50 which of the following statements would be *incorrect* regarding streptomycin?

    A It prevents the growth of tuberculosis bacteria
    B It is more effective against tuberculosis than cholera bacteria
    C It prevents the growth of cholera bacteria
    D It is more effective against tuberculosis than typhoid bacteria
    E It would be used to treat a patient suffering from typhoid.

16 An agar plate was prepared and a pure culture of a species of bacteria grown. 5 discs of filter paper were soaked in different strengths of the same disinfectant and placed on the agar. The plate was then incubated for three days at 37°C.

The results are shown in Fig. 51

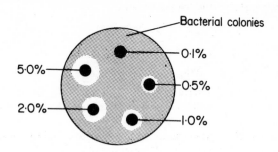

Fig. 51

Which of the following conclusions *cannot* safely be drawn from the results of this experiment?

    A Increasing the strength of the disinfectant increases its effectiveness

    B 5.0% is more effective than 2.0%.

    C 0.1% has no effect on the bacteria.

    D The bacteria are able to feed on a weak solution of the disinfectant.

    E 0.5% is as effective as 1.0%.

Multiple Completion

For each of the following incomplete statements or questions *one* or *more* of the responses numbered 1–4 are correct.

Choose the appropriate letter as your answer according to the following code

    A —if only 1, 2 and 3 are correct

    B —if only 1, 2 and 4 are correct

    C —if only 1 and 4 are correct

    D —if only 3 is correct

    E —if only 2, 3 and 4 are correct.

17 The head louse and the body louse

    1 produce eggs called 'nits'

    2 cannot move from one person to another

    3 spread syphilis

    4 can be controlled by DDT.

18 Contaminated milk may be responsible for the spread of

    1 tuberculosis

    2 smallpox

    3 cholera

    4 brucellosis.

19 Prophylactic measures in the fight against malaria include

   1 prevention of mosquitoes from breeding
   2 use of insecticides
   3 use of drugs in a healthy person
   4 confinement of the patient to bed.

20 Passive immunity may be acquired by

   1 passage of antibodies from mother to foetus during pregnancy
   2 production of antibodies in response to infection by pathogenic micro-organisms
   3 injection of a vaccine containing weakened or killed micro-organisms
   4 injection of a serum containing antitoxins.

21 Active immunity given by vaccination

   1 causes a mild form of the disease
   2 causes the production of antibodies
   3 gives immediate protection from the disease
   4 may last for a lifetime in the case of smallpox.

22 The release of toxins into the blood causes

   1 increased resistance to the pathogen
   2 an increase in body temperature
   3 an increase in activity of white cells
   4 production of antitoxins.

23 People associated with work on vaccination were

   1 Jenner
   2 Salk
   3 Calmette and Guérin
   4 Lister.

24 Which of the following pieces of equipment is (are) used for growing non-pathogenic bacteria in the laboratory?

   1 inoculating loop
   2 sterile lancet
   3 universal indicator solution
   4 petri dishes.

25 Three agar plates were prepared and the following treatments carried out. The subject placed his fingertips lightly on plate 1. The subject washed his hands in soap and water and dried them on a towel and then placed his fingertips on plate 2. The subject then scrubbed his hands thoroughly and dried them in hot air and then placed them on plate 3. The plates were then incubated for 2 days at 37° C. The results are shown in Fig. 52.

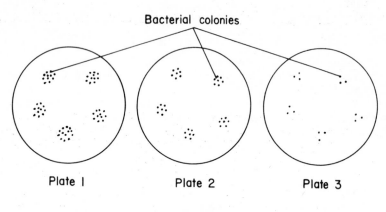

Fig. 52

Which of the following conclusions can be drawn from these results?

1 Bacteria are normally present on the skin.
2 The towel used was a dirty one.
3 Scrubbing the hands does not remove all bacteria from the skin.
4 The bacterial colonies on plate 3 came from the air in the room not from the fingers.

Matching Pairs

Each set of questions consist of five lettered headings **A, B, C, D** and **E** followed by four numbered items. Answer each question by choosing the *one* heading (**A, B, C, D** or **E**) that is related most closely to the item concerned.

EACH HEADING MAY BE USED ONCE, MORE THAN ONCE OR NOT AT ALL.

Questions 26–29

    A viruses
    B bacteria
    C protozoa
    D fungi
    E tapeworms

Which of the above are the causative organisms of

26 malaria?
27 cholera?
28 tuberculosis?
29 smallpox?

Questions 30–33

Which of the following diseases

    A psittacosis
    B rabies
    C cholera
    D typhus
    E septicaemia

are spread by

30 house-flies?
31 mites?
32 dogs?
33 parrots?

Questions 34–37

Which of the following methods of disease transmission

    A contaminated water
    B droplet infection
    C sexually transmitted
    D insect vector
    E contaminated food

is responsible for the spread of

34 cholera?
35 gonorrhea?
36 tuberculosis?
37 measles?

Questions 38–41

    A lice
    B house-flies
    C bed bugs
    D tsetse flies
    E mosquitoes

Which of the above insect vectors can be controlled by

38 spraying marshes with oil?
39 covering food in shops?
40 planting shrubs unacceptable as food?
41 washing hair with an insecticide?

Questions 42–45

A aetiology
B antitoxins
C diagnosis
D toxin
E prophylaxis

Which of the above is defined as

42 identification of a disease by its symptoms?
43 a poisonous substance produced by a microbe?
44 the study of the cause of a disease?
45 means of taking steps to reduce the chances of catching a particular disease?

Questions 46–49

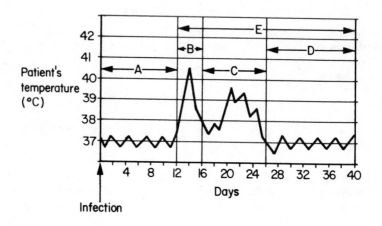

Fig. 53

Fig. 53 shows the stages in the development of a contagious disease from infection to recovery.

Match the periods A–E shown on Fig. 53 to the following

46 the incubation period
47 convalescence
48 the period during which the patient can spread the disease
49 the period in which a high fever is present.

Assertion/Reason

Each of the following questions consists of an *assertion* and a *reason*. Consider both statements and then choose the letter **A, B, C, D** or **E** as your answer according to the following

A—if both statements are true, and the reason is a correct explanation of the assertion

B —if both statements are true, but the reason is not a correct explanation of the assertion

C —if the assertion is true, but the reason is false

D —if the assertion is false, but the reason is true

E —if both statements are false.

Code Summarized

	ASSERTION	REASON	
A	true	true	reason is a correct explanation
B	true	true	reason is not a correct explanation
C	true	false	
D	false	true	
E	false	false	

	ASSERTION		REASON
50	Influenza is an infectious disease	*because*	influenza is caused by a virus.
51	Poliomyelitis is no longer a major threat to health in Britain	*because*	modern antiobiotics can cure the disease easily.
52	Spraying marshy ground with oil is used to control the spread of malaria	*because*	this is an effective way of denying the mosquitoes access to humans.
53	The number of deaths from tuberculosis has fallen over the last 50 years	*because*	a vaccine has been developed and people are screened by X-ray.
54	Quarantine is compulsory for animals entering this country	*because*	diseases can be brought into Britain by animals.
55	Plastic petri dishes are not used to grow bacteria	*because*	they cannot be sterilized by heat.

Structured Questions

56 Fig. 54 below shows the number of reported cases of tuberculosis and food poisoning in a country from 1964–1974.

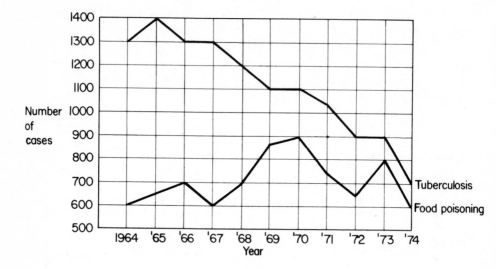

Fig. 54

a) Complete the table below to show the number of cases of each disease, the combined number for both diseases and the number of deaths from both diseases (assume the death rate for tuberculosis to be 1% of the cases and for food poisoning to be 2%).

YEAR	NUMBER OF CASES OF			TOTAL DEATHS
	TUBERCULOSIS	FOOD POISONING	BOTH	
1964				
1966				
1968				
1970				
1972				
1974				

b) Both these diseases are notifiable. What does this mean?
c) In which year was the number of cases of food poisoning the highest?
d) In which year was the number of cases of tuberculosis the highest?
e) Between which two years did the number of cases of tuberculosis fall by the greatest number?

f) Which disease shows a downward trend and which does not show a general fall in the number of cases over the 10-year period?

g) Suggest a reason for your answer to (f) above.

h) Is the information shown on the graph likely to represent an absolutely correct picture of the incidence of these two diseases in a community? Explain your answer.

57 a) From the following list of diseases choose the one which can be related to the description given in the table

(i) haemophilia

(ii) ringworm

(iii) gonorrhea

(iv) bilharziasis

(v) leukaemia

(vi) hydrophobia

(vii) scurvy

(viii) bubonic plague

(ix) cholera

(x) tuberculosis

(xi) diabetes

DESCRIPTION	DISEASE
Spread by sexual intercourse	
Can be transmitted by a dog bite	
Nutritional deficiency disease	
An inherited disease	
A form of cancer	
Caused by a fungus	
Spread by contaminated water	
Caused by a blood fluke	
Transmitted by the rat flea	
A lung disease	
Caused by a hormonal deficiency	

b) For each of the techniques or treatments listed below name *one* disease (not necessarily from the list above) which is most applicable to the technique or treatment

TECHNIQUE OR TREATMENT	DISEASE
Food inspection	
Mass chest radiography	
Strict quarantine regulations	
Chlorination of water	
Daily injections of insulin	
Prevention of mosquitoes from breeding	
Use of the Sabin vaccine	
Use of molluscicides	

c) Choose two of the techniques or treatments listed above and describe briefly what is involved in each.

58 a) Name six different ways by which pathogens may enter the body and for each state *one* disease which may result.

b) State three different ways in which the body reacts to the presence of pathogenic micro-organisms.

c) Before the advent of modern medicine, it was once fairly common practice to cover cuts or wounds with mouldy bread. Did this practice have a basis in fact?

59 The table below shows the number of deaths per 100,000 of the population for four diseases from 1900–1960

DISEASE	Year						
	1900	1910	1920	1930	1940	1950	1960
Tuberculosis	250	190	125	100	50	20	6
Heart disease	125	150	190	250	300	330	390
Diphtheria	50	45	30	20	10	5	0
Lung Cancer	5	5	15	25	75	110	360
Total No. of Deaths							

a) Complete the table to show the total number of deaths per year.

b) Using a single set of axes plot the number of deaths from the four diseases on a single graph. Name each curve.

c) Which two diseases have declined over the 60 years? Suggest a reason for this.

d) Suggest a reason for the increase in deaths from heart disease and lung cancer.

e) Name two techniques or treatments which have helped to cause the decrease in the number of deaths from tuberculosis.

f) What is the death rate from lung cancer likely to be in 1980, assuming there is no major discovery in the treatment of this disease — 450, 580, 620, 840, 980?

60 Explain the difference between

a) antiseptic and asepsis

b) active and passive immunity

c) infectious and contagious diseases

d) antibiotics and antibodies.

61 Briefly explain what is meant by each of the following

a) a vector

b) an antibiotic

c) a vaccine

d) a pathogen

e) aetiology

f) a serum

g) prophylaxis

h) an epidemic

i) a notifiable disease

j) a pandemic.

62   Four 10 cm³ samples of milk were taken in test tubes and 1 cm³ of a 0.005% solution of the dye resazurin was added to each. The four tubes were sealed with corks and incubated in a water bath as shown in Fig. 55.

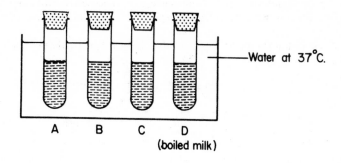

Fig. 55

Resazurin is a dye which colours milk blue. The dye changes colour when exposed to bacteria in milk. As the number of bacteria increases the dye changes from blue to pink and finally white.

After 1 hour's incubation the following results were obtained

        tube A — blue
        tube B — pink
        tube C — white
        tube D — blue.

a)   Why was the milk incubated at 37° C?
b)   How would you prepare a 0.005% solution of resazurin?
c)   Did tube A contain sterilised milk, sour milk or fresh, untreated milk? Explain your answer.
d)   Did tube B contain sterilised milk, sour milk or fresh, untreated milk? Explain your answer.
e)   Did tube C contain sterilised milk, sour milk or fresh, untreated milk? Explain your answer.
f)   Why did tube D remain blue?
g)   What was the purpose of tube D?

12. Social Hygiene

Multiple Choice

In each of the following questions choose *one* only of the letters **A, B, C, D** or **E** to indicate your answer.

1 Which of the following would provide the most comfortable conditions for a lounge?

	Temperature	Relative humidity
A	8°C	75
B	10°C	40
C	16°C	75
D	16°C	100
E	28°C	100

2 The most persistent litter problem is caused by

A tin cans
B cardboard boxes
C greaseproof paper
D plastic cups
E newspaper.

3 Which of the following gases would be most abundant in a stuffy, poorly-ventilated classroom after an hours lesson?

A carbon dioxide
B oxygen
C nitrogen
D carbon monoxide
E hydrogen

4 The establishment of smokeless zones has helped to lower the incidence of

A lung cancer
B heart disease
C bronchitis
D eye infections
E influenza.

5 Which of the following would *not* be affected by good ventilation?

A body temperature
B circulation of air
C humidity
D the risk of catching influenza
E the spread of contagious diseases.

6 To measure the humidity of the air one would use a

    A thermometer
    B humidifier
    C barometer
    D hygrometer
    E hydrometer.

7 Which of the following is incorporated into wallpaper paste?

    A a herbicide
    B an antibiotic
    C an insecticide
    D an anti-bacterial agent
    E a fungicide.

8 Heat from an electric fire is dispersed around a room by

    A radiation only
    B convection only
    C conduction and convection
    D radiation and convection
    E conduction only.

9 Fluoride is added to water in order to

    A soften the water
    B strengthen bones
    C kill germs
    D help prevent tooth decay
    E remove suspended particles from the water.

10 Which of the following foods can be preserved by both canning and freeze-drying?

    A peas
    B eggs
    C cereals
    D tomatoes
    E soft drinks.

11 Which of the following drugs can be obtained without a doctor's prescription?

    A penicillin
    B morphine
    C barbiturates
    D tetracycline
    E paracetamol.

Fig. 56

12 The animal shown in Fig. 56 is a

   A bed bug
   B body louse
   C rat flea
   D mosquito
   E tick.

13 The animal shown in Fig. 56 is a vector of

   A typhus
   B bubonic plague
   C malaria
   D Chagas' disease
   E sleeping sickness.

Fig. 57 shows the life-cycle of a human parasite. Study this diagram and then answer
questions 14–16.

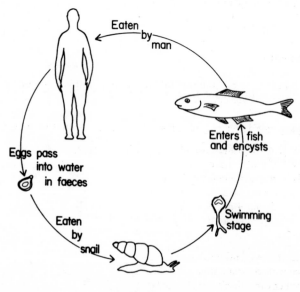

Fig. 57

14 The parasite is

    A a tapeworm
    B *Plasmodium*
    C a roundworm
    D a liver fluke
    E a trypanosome.

15 The swimming stage in Fig. 57 is termed a

    A cercaria
    B hydatid cyst
    C miracidium
    D nit
    E scolex.

16 Which of the following is the most practical method of preventing infection with the parasite shown in Fig. 57?

    A Kill all snails.
    B Immunize people to prevent infection.
    C Thoroughly cook all food.
    D Become a vegetarian.
    E Drain all ponds, rivers and marshy ground.

17 Which of the following would *not* result from continual heavy smoking?

    A depression of the nervous system
    B bronchitis
    C impairment of appetite and digestion
    D excessive production of mucus
    E impairment of judgement of distance.

Multiple Completion

For each of the following incomplete statements or questions *one* or *more* of the responses numbered 1–4 are correct.

Choose the appropriate letter as your answer according to the following code

    A — if only 1, 2 and 3 are correct
    B — if only 1, 2 and 4 are correct
    C — if only 1 and 4 are correct
    D — if only 3 is correct
    E — if only 2, 3 and 4 are correct.

18 Exercise causes

    1 lowering of the metabolic rate
    2 improvement in circulation
    3 improvement in muscle tone
    4 stimulation of appetite.

19 Ventilation in the home may be improved by the use of

  1 a humidifier
  2 fans
  3 air bricks
  4 louvred windows.

20 Which of the folllowing is (are) *essential* requirements for a hygenic kitchen?

  1 provision of hot and cold water
  2 easily cleaned wall tiles
  3 a fan mounted in the window
  4 a suitable means of waste disposal.

21 Which of the following types of heating reduce the humidity of the home?

  1 electric fire
  2 gas fire
  3 oil stove
  4 central heating.

22 Which of the following is (are) *essential* considerations when buying a house?

  1 The site should be well-drained.
  2 The house should have a concrete floor.
  3 It should have windows facing south so reducing heating bills.
  4 The house should have a damp-proof course.

23 Which of the following processes take place when water is stored in open reservoirs?

  1 the water settles to form the water table
  2 sedimentation
  3 aeration
  4 reduction in the numbers of harmful bacteria.

24 Bacteria in food may be killed by

  1 canning
  2 drying
  3 freezing
  4 salting.

25 Which of the following is (are) occupational diseases?

  1 lung cancer
  2 bronchitis
  3 asbestosis
  4 cystitis

Matching Pairs

Each set of questions consists of five lettered headings **A, B, C, D** and **E** followed by four numbered items. Answer each question by choosing the *one* heading (**A, B, C, D** or **E**) that is related most closely to the item concerned.

EACH HEADING MAY BE USED ONCE, MORE THAN ONCE OR NOT AT ALL.

Questions 26–29

    A Area Medical Officer
    B Environmental Health Inspector
    C Health visitor
    D Divisional Nursing Officer
    E General Practioner

Which of the above people

26 supervises the hygiene of shops and restaurants?

27 organises control measures to prevent epidemics?

28 has overall responsibility for providing vaccination centres?

29 gives vaccinations to people who intend travelling abroad?

Questions 30–33

    A U-bend
    B soil pipe
    C sewer pipe
    D house drain
    E septic tank

Which of the above

30 carries sewage away from the house?

31 prevents escape of gases from pipes and sewers?

32 receives waste from toilets?

33 must not have disinfectant put into it?

Questions 34–37

    A damp-proof course
    B cavity walls
    C broken air bricks
    D timber frames
    E absence of ceiling vents

Which of the above aspects of house construction would be responsible for

34 allowing rats to enter?

35 preventing water rising up the walls?

36 insulating against heat loss?

37 reducing ventilation?

Questions 38–41

    A sand filter bed
    B chlorination unit
    C settlement tanks
    D storage tanks
    E reservoirs

Which of the above parts of a water treatment plant

38 produces clear water, but with bacteria still present?

39 produces bacteria-free water?

40 stores pure water until it is needed by the consumer?

41 removes organic matter and large particles of debris?

Assertion/Reason

Each of the following questions consists of an *assertion* and a *reason*. Consider both statements and then choose the letter **A, B, C, D** or **E** as your answer according to the following.

    A —if both statements are true, and the reason is a correct explantion of the assertion
    B —if both statements are true, but the reason is not a correct explanation of the assertion
    C —if the assertion is true, but the reason is false
    D —if the assertion is false, but the reason is true
    E —if both statements are false.

Code Summarized

	ASSERTION	REASON	
A	true	true	reason is a correct explanation
B	true	true	reason is not a correct explanation
C	true	false	
D	false	true	
E	false	false	

	ASSERTION		REASON
42	Businessmen are less likely to die from heart disease than the average person	*because*	businessmen are generally subject to more stress and tension.
43	In some parts of the world desalination of sea water is used to provide drinking water	*because*	desalination is cheaper than other methods of water purification.
44	Chlorine is added to drinking water	*because*	chlorine helps to prevent tooth decay.

118

ASERTION		REASON
45 Vaccination against whooping cough is no longer used	*because*	whooping cough has been completely eradicated.
46 People suffering from athlete's foot need not be excluded from swimming lessons	*because*	the causative organism of athlete's foot cannot survive in water.

Structured Questions

47 Write *one* sentence to explain each of the following

    a) a damp-proof course

    b) the benefits of double-glazing

    c) smokeless zones

    d) artesian wells

    e) chlorination of water

    f) bacteriostatic food preservation

    g) the World Health Organisation

    h) advantages of central heating

    i) 'Blown' cans of food

    j) fluoridation of water.

48 a) Briefly explain the benefits to the individual or community of each of the following

    (i) mobile X-ray units
    (ii) ante-natal clinics
    (iii) family planning clinics
    (iv) eating fresh fruit
    (v) provision of adequate lighting in kitchens

    b) Briefly explain how each of the following may represent dangers to the health of the individual or community

    (i) rats
    (ii) house-flies
    (iii) an unlocked medicine chest within reach of a child
    (iv) storing poisons such as weedkillers in lemonade bottles
    (v) travelling on crowded buses or trains.

49 From the list of options given below choose *one* only and write it in the table against the item to which it is most closely related.

OPTIONS

air pollution, canning, earthquakes, filter beds, cervical smears, malaria, antibiotic, antiseptic, quarantine regulations, insulation, refrigeration, occupational disease, activated sludge, inherited disease, chest X-ray.

ITEM	OPTION
International travel	
Cavity walls	
Smokeless zones	
Water treatment	
Sir Ronald Ross	
Joseph Lister	
Mongolism	
Asbestosis	
Sewage disposal	
Food hygiene	
Tuberculosis	
Streptomycin	
Cholera epidemic	
Cancer of the womb	
Food preservation.	

50 a) Name three impurities that may be present in water and state the health hazards associated with each.

b) Arrange the following components of a water treatment plant in the correct order and briefly explain the function of each

   (i) settlement tank
   (ii) storage tank
   (iii) pump house
   (iv) chlorination unit
   (v) mains supply
   (vi) filter bed
   (vii) grid.

51 Fig. 58 shows the stages in sewage treatment.

a) Name the parts of the system numbered 1, 2 and 3.
b) What is the purpose of 1 and 2?
c) Explain how 3 works.
d) Explain, briefly, the part played by micro-organisms in the treatment of sewage.
e) State two uses to which the sludge in 2 may be put.

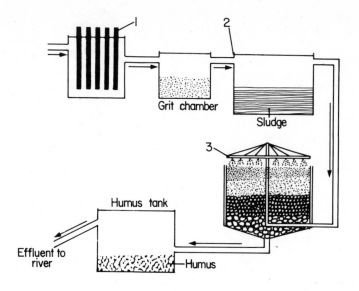

Grit chamber

Sludge

Humus tank

Effluent to
river

Humus

Fig.58

52 a) State five rules of hygiene that you would expect to be enforced in a food
       processing factory.
    b) Why are these rules necessary?
    c) State two reasons why food must be preserved.
    d) For each of the following foods state two ways in which it may be preserved
         (i) peas
         (ii) fish
         (iii) milk
         (iv) soups.
    e) Briefly describe the principle behind two of the methods of food preservation
       you have named in (d).

53 a) Name four industrial or occupational diseases together with the industry in
       which they occur.
    b) Choose two of the diseases and describe the measures that should be taken to
       prevent the disease.

Answers

1. Cells, Tissues, Organs and the Structure of the Body

1	D	11	C	21	A	31	D
2	C	12	B	22	C	32	A
3	D	13	E	23	D	33	B
4	B	14	E	24	C	34	C
5	D	15	B	25	B	35	D
6	D	16	E	26	B	36	B
7	D	17	C	27	E	37	E
8	B	18	D	28	B	38	A
9	B	19	E	29	C	39	E
10	D	20	A	30	A		

40 a) 1 Cell membrane
    2 Mitochondrion
    3 Golgi body
    4 Nucleolus
    5 Nucleus
    6 Nuclear membrane
    7 Nuclear pore
    8 Lysosome
    9 Endoplasmic reticulum.   (9)
  b) 1 Controls entry and exit of substances to and from cell
    2 Produces ATP
    5 Controls activity of cell.   (3)
  c)   Chromosomes.
  d)   During cell division.
  e)   Shows all the features which the majority of human cells have in common.   (3)

f) (i)   No nucleus, biconcave-disc shape   (2)
    (ii) Dendrites, elongated axon/myelin sheath   (2)
    (iii) Elongated shape, actin and myosin filaments   (2)
    (iv) Tail, head region/spiral mitochondria   (2)

41 a) 1   Motor neurone
           2   White blood cell
           3   Smooth muscle cell
           4   Red blood cell
           5   Ciliated epithelial cell
           6   Spermatozoon   (6)
    b)   1   Spinal cord/nerve in arm (allow others)
           2   Blood
           3   Intestines/arteries (allow others)
           4   Blood
           5   Lining of trachea/bronchi
           6   Testes/seminal vesicles/seminiferous tubules/vas deferens   (6)
    c)   1   Conducts impulses from C.N.S. to effectors
           2   Ingests bacteria/produce antibodies
           3   Causes movement
           4   Transports oxygen
           5   Moves mucus and particles up the trachea
           6   Fertilises egg/provides paternal chromosomes   (6)
    d)   1   Elongated axon/dendrites/myelin sheath/node of Ranvier
           2   Lobed nucleus
           3   Can contract/spindle-shaped
           4   Contains haemoglobin/biconcave-disc shape/lacks a nucleus
           5   Cilia
           6   Tail/head region/spiral mitochondria.   (6)

42 a) (i)   Liver
           (ii) Water, bile salts/bile pigments
           (iii) Emulsifies fats/neutralises acids.   (5)
    b)   (i)   Sweat glands
           (ii) Water, sodium chloride/traces of urea and amino acids
           (iii) Evaporation reduces body temperature.   (5)
    c)   (i)   Salivary glands
           (ii) Salivary amylase, water/mucus
           (iii) Digests starch/lubricates food.   (5)
    d)   (i)   Mammary glands
           (ii) Fat, protein/water/lactose/salts/vitamins
           (iii) Food for baby   (5)
    e)   (i)   Tear glands
           (ii) Water, sodium chloride/sodium bicarbonate/lysozyme
           (iii) Keeps conjunctiva moist/removes dust from eye.   (5)
    f)   (i)   Kidney
           (ii) Water, salts/urea/ammonia/uric acid
           (iii) Removes excretory products from body.   (5)

g) (i) Stomach
    (ii) Pepsin, rennin/water/mucus/hydrochloric acid
    (iii) Digests proteins to polypeptides/rennin clots milk.   (5)

43 a)

1	Trachea	8	Ileum
2	Ribs	9	Bladder
3	Left lung	10	Appendix
4	Heart	11	Colon
5	Diaphragm	12	Abdominal cavity
6	Stomach	13	Gall bladder
7	Pancreas	14	Liver. (14)

b) X over the position of the pancreas
c) Spleen, kidney, ureters/abdominal blood vessels/ovaries in
    female.   (3)
d) (i) 14   (v) 7/8
    (ii) 3   (vi) 13
    (iii) 6   (vii) 1.   (7)
    (iv) 8

2. Food and Diet

1	D	12	E	23	A	34	D
2	C	13	E	24	E	35	C
3	D	14	B	25	B	36	A
4	D	15	C	26	A	37	D
5	E	16	D	27	E	38	C
6	A	17	A	28	C	39	A
7	D	18	C	29	E	40	A
8	B	19	C	30	C	41	C
9	B	20	A	31	A	42	D
10	D	21	B	32	B		
11	D	22	B	33	B		

43 a) 1 Provides amino acids for growth—fish, steak   (2)
         2 Energy source/energy storage—butter, cheese   (2)
         3 Energy source—potatoes, sugar   (2)
         4 Haemoglobin formation—liver, eggs   (2)
         5 Blood clotting—peas, tomatoes   (2)
         6 Metabolic reactions take place in solution/for production of various
            secretions—milk, drinking water   (2)
         7 Stimulates peristalsis in colon—cabbage, lettuce. (Allow others)   (2)
      b)   Xerophthalmia—lack of vitamin A   (2)
            Scurvy—lack of vitamin C   (2)
            Anaemia—lack of iron. (Allow others)   (2)

44 a)   Added to prevent deficiency in areas where iodides are absent from
            drinking water.   (4)
      b)   Useful to people liable to deficiency. Essential in some cases such as baby
            foods and foods which have the natural vitamin content reduced by
            methods of processing. Possibly also a 'sales gimmick'.   (4)

c)   Ideal for a very young baby, not for adults because of lack of iron and high water content. Contains protein, fat, carbohydrate, vitamins, minerals and water. Lacking in some vitamins, minerals and roughage.   (4)

d)   Source of vitamin C—prevents scurvy. Also contains traces of other vitamins and some minerals.   (4)

45 a)   Group B—rapid growth with a 70% increase in weight.
Group A—slight weight increase for 13 days then fall in weight to just above original weight. (4)

b)   (i) Growth continues to day 37 then average weight falls off rapidly
    (ii) Continue to lose weight for 4 days then average weight increases rapidly.   (4)

c)   Milk contains accessory food factors essential for normal growth adds extra nutrients to a diet which contains insufficient quantities of them.   (2)

(d)   To prevent errors arising from possible peculiar growth of one animal. Allows more valid conclusions to be drawn from results.   (2)

e)   Continued fall in weight, symptoms of vitamin deficiency, possible death.   (3)

46 a)   Carbohydrates and fats contain carbon, hydrogen and oxygen only, proteins also contain nitrogen, phosphorus and sulphur.   (2)

b)   Cheese, meat, fish, eggs, beans, nuts/or others.   (6)

c)   Biuret and Millons.   (2)

Millons — crush food in water, add half the volume of Millon's reagent and boil gently. Precipitated pink or red mass indicates protein.

Biuret — crush food in water, add an equal volume of 5% sodium hydroxide solution and two drops of 1% copper sulphate solution. A pink or violet colour indicates protein.   (5)

47 a)   Protein—Millon's reagent or Biuret
Reducing sugar—Fehling's or Benedict's reagent.
Starch—iodine solution   (3)

b)

FOOD	PROTEIN TEST	STARCH TEST	REDUCING SUGAR TEST
Milk	Red/violet	Brown	Red
Potatoes	Clear colour	Blue-black	Blue
Cheese	Red/violet	Brown	Blue
Table sugar	Clear colour	Brown	Blue
Fish	Red/violet	brown	Blue

(6)

c)   Milk—contains protein and reducing sugar but no starch.   (3)
Potatoes—contain starch only   (3)
Cheese—contains protein only.   (3)
Table sugar—contains no protein, starch or reducing sugar.   (3)
Fish—contains protein only.   (3)

d)   Cheese, milk/fish.   (2)

e)   Mix food thoroughly with ether, pour liquid onto filter paper, translucent grease spot indicates fat/emulsion test.   (4)

48 a)

PERSON	ENERGY REQUIREMENT PER DAY (kilojoules)
Coal miner	16500
11 year old boy	10500
Athlete in training	19000
Typist	10500
2 year old child	6000
Nursing mother	10000

(3)

b)   Age, occupation, sex, size.   (4)
c)   8000kJ.
d)   Carbohydrates and fats.   (2)

3.   Nutrition and Digestion

1	D	11	E	21	B	31	E
2	D	12	D	22	A	32	A
3	A	13	E	23	C	33	C
4	E	14	E	24	E	34	B
5	C	15	C	25	B	35	E
6	E	16	A	26	C	36	E
7	C	17	C	27	C	37	A
8	D	18	C	28	A	38	A
9	E	19	D	29	D	39	B
10	E	20	D	30	B	40	E

41 a)   1   Oesophagus   6   Rectum
        2   Stomach   7   Appendix
        3   Pancreas   8   Bile duct
        4   Colon   9   Gall bladder
        5   Ileum   10   Liver.   (10)
    b)   At base of stomach.
    c)   Closes off exit from stomach and retains food.   (2)
    d)   In pancreas.
    e)   Insulin.
    f)   10.
    g)   2.
    h)   Digests proteins to polypeptides.   (2)
    i)   In ileum
    j)   Hepatic portal vein.
    k)   (i) Stored as glycogen   (2)
         (ii) Deaminated to urea.   (2)

42 a)

	IODINE TEST		FEHLING'S (BENEDICT'S) TEST	
	A	B	A	B
At start	Brown	Brown	Blue	Blue
After 30 mins.	Brown	Brown	Red	Blue

(2)

b)   A.

c)   Amylase/diastase.

d)   Reducing sugar.

e)   Bloodstream.

f)   Impermeable to starch.

g)   To demonstrate enzyme is necessary for digestion.   (2)

h)   Little or no reducing sugar formed—pH too low for enzyme activity.   (3)

i)   Boil test material gently with Fehling's or Benedict's reagent—note colour change.   (3)

43 a)   37° C—optimum temperature for enzyme activity.   (2)

b)   Tubes labelled and placed in water bath.   (2)

c)   To determine presence or absence of starch.

d)   No starch present.

e)   Both contain starch.

f)   1 and 3.   (2)

g)   Salivary amylase, pancreatic amylase.   (2)

h)   Boil a small sample gently with Fehling's or Benedict's reagent and record any colour change. Tubes 1 and 3—red colour. Tubes 2 and 4—no colour change.   (7)

i)   Enzymes are denatured and activity ceases.   (2)

44 a)   Ileum

b)   1   Blood capillary

   2   Lacteal

   3   Epithelium

   4   Lymphatic vessel.   (4)

c)   1

d)   2

e)   Thin epithelium, large surface area/blood capillaries close to surface. (2)

f)   Hepatic portal vein.

45 a)   Fat.

b)   Lipase.

c)   Blue.

d)   1 yellow, 2 blue, 3 yellow.   (3)

e)   1 acid, 2 alkaline, 3 acid.   (3)

f)   Production of fatty acids from fat digestion.

g)   Bile salts emulsify fats exposing a greater surface to the action of the enzyme—rate of reaction increases.   (2)

h)   To demonstrate that they speed up fat digestion.   (2)

i)   Enzyme is denatured.

46 a)	Colon.	i)	Pancreas.
b)	Glucose.	j)	Villus.
c)	Chyme.	k)	Liver.
d)	Deamination.	l)	Ileum.
e)	Rickets.	m)	Duodenum.
f)	Glycerol.	n)	Peristalsis.
g)	Pyloric sphincter.	o)	Ascorbic acid. (15)
h)	Amylase.		

4.   Respiration

1	C	13	B	25	E	37	C
2	D	14	E	26	C	38	A
3	B	15	B	27	C	39	D
4	C	16	B	28	E	40	E
5	B	17	C	29	A	41	B
6	E	18	C	30	E	42	D
7	C	19	B	31	A	43	A
8	E	20	B	32	C	44	A
9	A	21	B	33	B	45	A
10	D	22	C	34	A	46	D
11	C	23	A	35	B		
12	E	24	A	36	D		

47 a)   Diaphragm contracts and intercostal muscles contract—diaphragm moves down and ribs and sternum move up and out. Volume of thorax and lungs is increased and the pressure is lowered below atmospheric pressure. Atmospheric pressure forces air into the lungs through the nasal cavity, larynx, trachea, bronchi, bronchioles and into alveoli. During expiration muscles of diaphragm and ribs relax and these organs return to their original positions. Elastic nature of lungs causes them to contract and expel air.   (10)

b)   (i) Increases—due to increased carbon dioxide concentration of the blood.   (3)

(ii) Little effect—receptors are only stimulated by large falls in oxygen concentration.   (3)

48 a)   Large surface area to volume ratio, thin membrane, moist surface/excellent blood supply.   (3)

b)   Production of energy which is made available in ATP in the mitochondria of the cells from glucose and oxygen with the production of water and carbon dioxide as waste products.   (2)

c)   Nasal cavity—larynx—trachea—bronchus—bronchiole—alveolus—red blood cell,—pulmonary vein—left atrium—left venticle—aorta—renal artery—capillary—tissue fluid—kidney cell.   (15)

49 a)

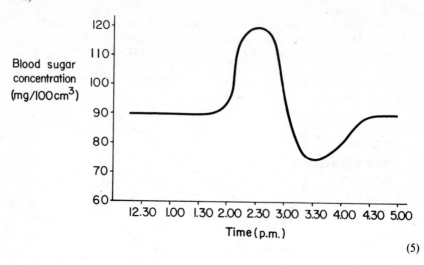

Time (p.m.)

(5)

b)   90mg/100cm³.
c)   (i) 120mg/100cm³.
    (ii) 75mg/100cm³.
d)   (i) 92mg/100cm³.
    (ii) 75mg/100cm³.
   (iii) 82mg/100cm³.
e)   60 minutes.
f)   i) Sharp rise in blood sugar level after 30 minutes caused by rapid absorption
         of glucose   (2)
     (ii) To supply energy   (2)
g)   Vigorous activity depletes blood sugar.   (2)
h)   Stored glycogen is converted to glucose to prevent excessive fall in blood
        sugar level.   (2)
i)   When blood sugar rises pancreas secretes insulin which causes conversion
        of glucose to glycogen thereby restoring normal blood sugar level. When
        level of blood sugar falls insulin production is reduced and less glucose is
        converted to glycogen—level of blood sugar tends to rise to normal
        level.   (6)

50 a)

SPEED (km/hour)	NUMBER OF BREATHS (per minute)	VOLUME OF EACH BREATH (litres)	VOLUME OF AIR BREATHED PER MINUTE (litres)
2	15	0.8	12.0
5	17	1.6	27.2
7	19	2.0	38.0
9	20	2.5	50.0

(4)

b)   1.7 litres.

c)   38.0 litres.

d)   Increased speed requires more energy therefore greater oxygen demand. Increased rate of respiration causes increase in carbon dioxide concentration of blood which leads to increase in rate of breathing. (4)

e)

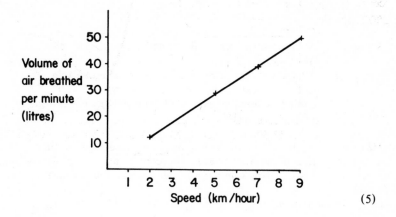

(5)

5. Blood and Circulation

1	B	11	E	21	C	31	A
2	E	12	A	22	B	32	E
3	E	13	D	23	B	33	D
4	D	14	E	24	B	34	B
5	A	15	E	25	B	35	A
6	E	16	C	26	D	36	C
7	A	17	E	27	D	37	A
8	D	18	C	28	C	38	D
9	D	19	B	29	E	39	C
10	C	20	E	30	D	40	C

41 a)   1   Urea—
        (i) Liver
        (ii) Kidney
        (iii) Transported excretory product.   (3)
     2   Lactic acid—
        (i) Skeletal muscles
        (ii) Liver
        (iii) Product of anaerobic respiration.   (3)
     3   Glucose—
        (i) Ileum
        (ii) Cells/Liver
        (iii) Transported respiratory substrate.   (3)

4 Carbon dioxide—
(i) Cells
(ii) Lungs
(iii) Transported excretory product (3)
5 Antibodies—
(i) Lymphocytes/plasma cells of connective tissue
(ii) Site of infection
(iii) Neutralise bacterial toxins. (3)

b) 1 After a protein-rich meal—Renal artery/hepatic vein (2)
    2 After vigorous exercise—Iliac vein (2)
    3 After a carbohydrate-rich meal—Hepatic portal vein (2)
    4 After vigorous exercise—Pulmonary artery (2)
    5 During bacterial infection—Blood capillaries close to site of infection. (2)

42 a) Production of antibodies, ingestion of bacteria/clotting. (2)
    b) Hepatic portal vein has a higher concentration of glucose and amino acids, hepatic vein has a higher concentration of urea. (3)
    c)

Front view   Side view

Cytoplasm   Polymorphic nucleus

Red blood cell lacking a nucleus

Biconcave — disc shaped

White blood cell
Irregular shape
with large rounded
or lobed nucleus

(10)

43 a) 1 Pulmonary vein   5 Mesenteric artery
    2 Aorta   6 Hepatic vein
    3 Hepatic artery   7 Inferior vena cava
    4 Hepatic portal vein   8 Pulmonary artery. (8)
    b)   1, 2, 3, 5. (4)
    c)   Right and left atria (auricles), right and left venticles. (4)
    d)   Right atrium, right ventricle. (2)
    e) 1 arrow towards heart
    2 arrow in either direction
    4 arrow towards liver
    8 arrow towards lungs. (4)
    f)   Blood passes through heart twice during a complete circulation of the body. (3)

44 a) 1   Aorta
     2   Pulmonary artery
     3   Pulmonary vein
     4   Bicuspid valve
     5   Left ventricle
     6   Right ventricle
     7   Tricuspid valve
     8   Inferior vena cava
     9   Right atrium (auricle)
    10   Superior vena cava.   (10)

   b) X   deoxygenated
      Y   oxygenated.   (2)

   c) A   arrow into pulmonary artery
      B   arrow into aorta.   (2)

   d)   (i) Transports glucose/urea/hormones/amino acids   (2)
      (ii) Produce clotting factors   (2)
      (iii) Ingest bacteria/produce antibodies.   (2)

45 a)

Recipient

		O	A	B	AB
	O	√	√	√	√
Donor	A	x	√	x	√
	B	x	x	√	√
	AB	x	x	x	√

                (16)

  b)   Universal donor—person of blood group? O—can donate blood to a recipient of any group without causing agglutination.   (2)

       Universal recipient—person of blood group AB—can receive blood from any group without agglutination.   (2)

46 a)   Complex series or reactions which convert soluble fibrinogen to insoluble fibrin. Caused by disintegration of platelets on exposure to air. Requires vitamin K and calcium ions. Prevents excessive bleeding and entry of germs.   (5)

  b)   Swelling of an artery resulting from pressure of heart—gives an indication of rate of heart beat. Usually felt where an artery lies over a bone close to the skin surface.   (5)

  c)   Swellings on lymphatic vessels—produce antibodies and white blood cells. Also remove harmful bacteria from lymph. May swell during infection eg. tonsils.   (5)

  d)   Transfer of blood from one person to another. Needed, usually, after extensive blood loss. Four blood groups—A, B, AB and O. Recipient's blood should not contain antibodies corresponding to donor's antigens. As a result only certain blood types are compatible. In Britian blood is given voluntarily and stored at low temperatures until needed.   (5)

47 a)   Blood from which fibrin has been removed.   (2)
    b)   To prevent clotting.   (2)
    c)   Blood cells absorb water by osmosis and burst.   (2)
    d)   Haemoglobin released into solution.   (2)

e)   0.9% sodium chloride is isotonic with human blood, therefore no net movement of water into or out of cells.   (2)

f)

Normal red blood cell

Red blood cell
from tube C   (4)

g)   Osmosis.

6. Excretion and the Skin

1	A	11	A	21	E	31	A
2	D	12	B	22	B	32	A
3	E	13	B	23	A	33	E
4	E	14	E	24	C	34	C
5	A	15	C	25	B	35	B
6	A	16	E	26	C	36	A
7	E	17	E	27	B	37	A
8	A	18	C	28	C		
9	B	19	B	29	E		
10	E	20	B	30	B		

38 a)   Capillaries dilate—more blood flows to skin—more heat lost to the atmosphere.   (2)

b)   Determines skin colour and absorbs ultra-violet radiation.   (2)

c)   After prolonged sweating production of sweat ceases. Body temperature rises to a fatal level. Caused by prolonged vigorous activity at high temperatures.   (2)

d)   Humid conditions slow down or prevent evaporation of sweat. Body temperature rises causing collapse and possible death.   (2)

e)   Large amounts of salt lost in sweat. Unless replaced salt balance of blood i upset leading to heat cramp.   (2)

39 a)   Increased quantity of urine with a higher concentration of water—less ADH secreted.   (3)

b)   Glucose appears in urine—cannot be stored therefore blood glucose level rises until it is excreted.   (3)

c)   No AHD secreted—less water reabsorbed—large quantities of watery urine produced.   (3)

d)   Excess amino acids converted to urea—more urea appears in urine.(3)

e)   ADH secreted—less water excreted—a more concentrated urine produced.   (3)

40 a)   1   Aorta   5   Bladder
2   Left renal vein   6   Right renal artery
3   Left kidney   7   Right renal vein
4   Ureter   8   Posterior vena cava.   (8)

b) 2 Takes filtered blood away from kidney
    3 Excretes urea/regulates water balance of body/excretes salts
    4 Takes urine to bladder
    5 Stores urine
    6 Takes blood to kidney.   (5)
c)

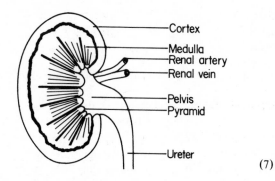

Cortex
Medulla
Renal artery
Renal vein
Pelvis
Pyramid
Ureter

(7)

41 a) Process by which metabolic waste products are removed from the body.   (3)
b) Carbon dioxide—lungs
    Urea—kidneys/skin
    Water—kidneys/lungs/skin
    Salts—kidneys/skin
    Ammonia—kidneys.   (10)
c) High pressure in glomerulus causes fluid to filter from blood into Bowman's capsule. Fluid contains water, glucose, amino acids, salts and nitrogenous waste. All glucose, amino acids and some water are reabsorbed in proximal tubule. Some salts reabsorbed in distal tubule. Remaining fluid is concentrated by reabsorption of water in collecting duct—remaining fluid is urine.   (12)

42 a) 1 Blood capillary   6 Proximal convoluted tubule
        2 Efferent blood vessel   7 Loop of Henle
        3 Afferent blood vessel   8 Distal convoluted tubule
        4 Glomerulus   9 Collecting duct.   (9)
        5 Bowman's capsule
b) Arrow towards capsule.
c) Proximal tubule.
d) Collecting duct.
e) Excretion of urea/water/salts
    Regulation of pH of blood
    Regulation of water balance of body.   (3)
f) (i) Becomes concentrated in urine
    (ii) Reabsorbed into blood
    (iii) Some reabsorbed, some excreted.   (3)
g) 9.
h) Urine.

43 a)   1   Cornified layer
        2   Granular layer
        3   Malpighian layer
        4   Sweat duct
        5   Erector muscle
        6   Blood capillaries
        7   Sweat gland
        8   Adipose (fatty) tissue
        9   Nerve ending
     10   Meissner's corpuscle
     11   Sebaceous gland.   (11)

b)   Produces epidermal cells/absorbs ultra-violet radiation.

c)   Sebum.

d)   Waterproofs hair/prevents epidermis from drying out.

e)   6—May dilate or constrict therefore bringing more or less blood to the skin. Regulate amount of heat lost by convection and radiation.   (2)

         7—Produce sweat which forms a layer on skin surface—as this evaporates, heat is taken from skin thus reducing body temperature.Sweat production can be controlled.   (2)

         8—Insulating properties reduce heat loss.   (2)

7.   The Skeleton, Muscles and Movement

1	B	**11**	A	**21**	E	**31**	A
2	D	**12**	A	**22**	C	**32**	C
3	D	**13**	E	**23**	A	**33**	B
4	A	**14**	E	**24**	B	**34**	C
5	E	**15**	B	**25**	E	**35**	D
6	A	**16**	B	**26**	A	**36**	C
7	A	**17**	E	**27**	B	**37**	A
8	C	**18**	C	**28**	C	**38**	D
9	C	**19**	C	**29**	D	**39**	D
10	C	**20**	D	**30**	E		

40 a)   1   Scapula
        2   Femur
        3   Rib
        4   Atlas vertebra.   (4)

b)   A   Humerus
        B   Pelvic girdle
        C   Tibia
        D   Thoracic vertebrae.   (4)

c)   1

d)   A   Ball and socket
        B   Ball and socket
        C   Hinge.   (3)

e)

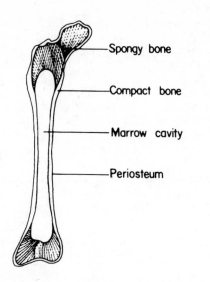

—Spongy bone

—Compact bone

—Marrow cavity

—Periosteum

(6)

41 a)   1   Ball and socket
        5   Hinge.   (2)
  b)   1   Allows movement in three planes   (2)
        5   Allows movement in one plane.   (2)
  c)   3   Humerus
        6   Radius.   (2)
  d)   Paired muscles, each producing movement in opposite directions.
            Necessary since muscles cannot lengthen.   (2)
  e)   2   Biceps
        4   Triceps.   (2)
  f)   Arrow towards scapula.
  g)   2.
  h)   Hip.

42 a)

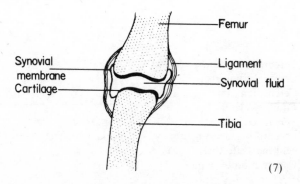

—Femur

Synovial
membrane

Cartilage—

—Ligament

—Synovial fluid

—Tibia

(7)

137

b) (i) Lubricant
    (ii) Prevents friction
    (iii) Hold bones together.   (3)

43 a)   Pelvis and leg. Pelvic girdle and femur.   (3)
   b)   1   Pelvis
        3   Patella
        4   Tibia
        5   Fibula
        7   Femur.   (5)
   c)   6.
   d)   2.
   e)   Hinge.
   f)   Movement in one plane.   (2)
   g)   Ball and socket.
   h)   Tarsals.

8. Nervous and Hormonal Co-ordination

1	D	12	D	23	E	34	E
2	A	13	C	24	D	35	D
3	C	14	C	25	B	36	C
4	A	15	E	26	A	37	B
5	E	16	B	27	C	38	E
6	E	17	C	28	D	39	B
7	E	18	A	29	B	40	A
8	C	19	B	30	D	41	A
9	B	20	D	31	B	42	D
10	B	21	B	32	C	43	A
11	A	22	C	33	E		

44 a)   (i) 5
        (ii) 3
        (iii) 1
        (iv) 2
        (v) 4   (5)
   b)   (i) Cerebral hemisphere
        (ii) Cerebral hemisphere
        (iii) Cerebellum
        (iv) Pituitary gland
        (v) Spinal cord.   (5)
   c)   Receptor—sensory neurone—intermediate neurone—motor
        neurone—effector.   (5)
   d)   Constriction of pupil.

45 a)

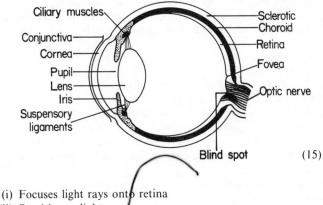

Ciliary muscles

Conjunctiva

Cornea

Pupil

Lens

Iris

Suspensory ligaments

Sclerotic

Choroid

Retina

Fovea

Optic nerve

Blind spot   (15)

b) (i) Focuses light rays onto retina
   (ii) Sensitive to light
   (iii) Alters shape of lens
   (iv) Transmits impulses from eye to brain.   (4)

c) Eye originally accommodated for near vision. Circular muscle fibres in ciliary body relax. Suspensory ligaments become taut causing lens to flatten and become less convex. Circular muscles of iris relax and longtitudinal muscles contract dilating pupil. Image of plane is focused on retina.   (6)

46 a)

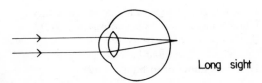

Long sight

Light rays from a near object come into focus behind the retina. Caused by an eyeball which is too short or a lens which is too thin.

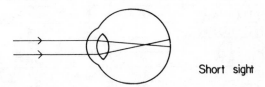

Short sight

Light rays from a distant object are focused in front of retina. Caused by an eyeball which is too long or a lens which is too fat.   (10)

b) Long sight—wear spectacles with convex lenses which cause light rays to converge.
Short sight—wear spectacles with concave lenses which cause light rays to diverge.   (4)

c)   Sound waves cause the eardrum to vibrate and the vibrations are transmitted through the ear ossicles to the smaller oval window, thus concentrating the force of vibration. This causes oscillations in the fluid of the inner ear. Vibrations of fluid in the cochlea stimulate receptor cells which send nerve impulses along auditory nerve to the brain.   (6)

47 a) (i) Pupil dilates
      (ii) Pupil closes
  b) (i) By contraction of radial muscles of iris (2)
      (ii) By contraction of circular muscles of iris (2)
  c) (i) Blind spot is the part where the optic nerve passes through the retina. Contains no light sensitive cells (3)
      (ii) Fovea is a small depression in centre of retina containing only cones. It enables maximum perception of images in conditions of good illumination (3)
     (iii) Protein-containing gel between lens and retina. Helps to maintain shape of eye and also refracts light (3)

48 a)   1   Pinna
      2   External auditory meatus
      3   Tympanic membrane
      4   Malleus
      5   Incus
      5   Stapes
      7   Semicircular canals
      8   Auditory nerve
      9   Cochlea
     10 Eustachian tube.   (10)
  b)   2   Transmits sound waves into ear/secretes wax   (2)
      3   Vibrates in response to sound waves   (2)
      6   Transmits vibrations to oval window   (2)
      7   Detects movement and balance   (2)
      8   Transmits impulses to brain   (2)
     10 Equalises air pressure on either side of eardrum. (2)
  c)   2   Excessive secretion of wax
     10 Blockage by mucus during a cold.   (2)
  d) 8/9

49

GLAND	HORMONE	FUNCTION
PITUITARY	4	7
THYROID	3	8
ADRENAL	5	12
OVARY	6	10
PANCREAS	1	9
TESTIS	2	11

(12)

9. Growth and Reproduction

1	A	12	B	23	A	34	B
2	E	13	A	24	A	35	A
3	E	14	D	25	C	36	C
4	E	15	E	26	B	37	B
5	D	16	B	27	C	38	A
6	B	17	C	28	A	39	A
7	E	18	B	29	D	40	A
8	E	19	C	30	E	41	C
9	D	20	B	31	A	42	C
10	B	21	C	32	E	43	C
11	E	22	D	33	D		

44 a)   1   Oviduct/fallopian tube
      2   Ovary
      3   Uterus
      4   Uterus wall
      5   Vagina.   (5)
   b)   (i) 2
      (ii) 5
      (iii) 1
      (iv) 4
      (v) 4.   (5)
   c)   (i) Arrows along oviduct, uterus and through vagina   (2)
      (ii) At base of uterus
      (iii) On upper uterus wall.

45 a)   14—body temperature rises.   (2)
   b)   37°C.
   c)   From day 15 to day 26.
   d)   'Rhythm' method.
   e)   Woman's cycle may be irregular
          Temperature fluctuations may be caused by other factors.   (2)
   f)   13–15.
   g)   From day 5 to day 10 and day 18 to day 28.   (2)

46 a)   1   Foetus
      2   Uterus
      3   Rectum
      4   Pubic bone
      5   Bladder
      6   Umbilical cord
      7   Placenta.   (7)
   b)   Holds foetus during pregnancy, contracts at birth.   (2)
   c)   Allows exchange of respiratory gases/glucose/urea between foetal and maternal blood, secretes hormones.   (2)
   d)   Carries food and oxygen to foetus/waste products from foetus.
   e)   8/9 months.
   f)   Contraction of uterus wall.
   g)   Iron.

FUNCTION	STRUCTURE
Contracts at birth	UTERUS
Produces eggs	OVARY
Produces sperms	TESTES
A structure in which fertilization occurs	FALLOPIAN TUBE
Connects the embryo to the placenta	UMBILICAL CORD
Produces milk	MAMMARY GLAND
Produces oxytocin	PITUITARY GLAND
Carries both sperm and urine	URETHRA
Carries urine only	URETER
Allows the foetus to obtain food and oxygen	PLACENTA (10)

48 a)
1	Kidney	5	Uterus	
2	Ureter	6	Cervix	
3	Oviduct/fallopian tube	7	Vagina	
4	Ovary	8	Bladder.	(8)

b) (i) 4   (iv) 4
(ii) 8   (v) 5
(iii) 1   (vi) 5   (6)
c) 7–6–5–3. (4)
d) Bladder.

49 a) 23. Meiosis/Reduction division. (2)
b) 46.
c) Mitosis.
d) Fertilization of eggs by sperm, each with 23 chromosomes results in a zygote with diploid number of chromosomes i.e. 46. (3)
e) (i)

AGE (months)	WEIGHT (grams)	INCREASE IN WEIGHT (grams)
3	50	—
4	150	100
5	300	150
6	650	350
7	1200	550
8	1700	500
9	2250	550
Birth	3250	1000 (7)

(ii)

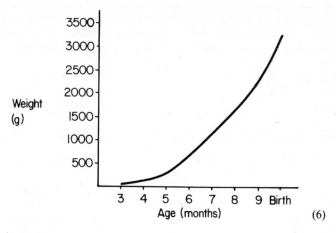

Weight (g)

Age (months)

(6)

(iii) 9 and birth
(iv) 3 and 4
(v) 3 to 4
(vi) Increase in size of foetus.   (2)

10.   Inheritance and Populations

1	C	13	A	25	C	37	B
2	D	14	E	26	A	38	D
3	E	15	E	27	B	39	C
4	C	16	E	28	C	40	E
5	E	17	E	29	E	41	A
6	D	18	C	30	A	42	A
7	A	19	A	31	C	43	B
8	B	20	A	32	D	44	B
9	E	21	C	33	B	45	E
10	C	22	B	34	D	46	A
11	A	23	E	35	A	47	A
12	C	24	C	36	C		

48 a)   (i) All brown hair
(ii) Half children with brown hair, half with red hair.   (2)

b)   (i) An organism which is homozygous has identical members of a given pair of genes i.e. BB or bb. An heterozygote has a pair of contrasing genes i.e. Bb.   (4)

(ii) Genotype refers to the genetic constitution of the organism.
Phenotype refers to the observable characteristics of an organism.
Individuals of the same phenotype may have different genotypes i.e. people with brown eyes may have the genotype BB or Bb.   (4)

(iii) A dominant gene is one which expresses itself in the phenotype at the exclusion of the other member of the allelic pair.
A recessive gene lacks the ability to express itself when the dominant gene is present and the characteristic controlled by the gene is only expressed in the phenotype when the gene is homozygous.   (4)

49 a)

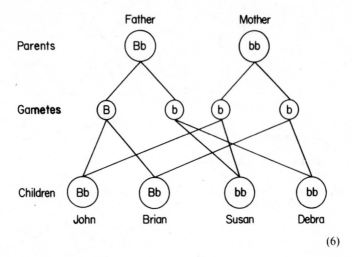

(6)

b)   Brown. Father cannot have blue eyes otherwise all children would be blue-eyed. Brian must have brown eyes since he inherits the gene for brown eyes from his father.   (2)

c)   Brown to blue eyes in a 1:1 ratio.   (2)

50 a)

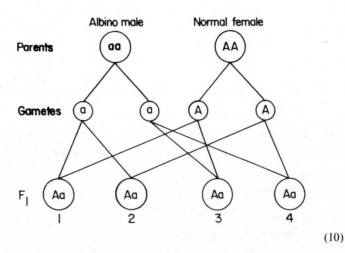

(10)

b)

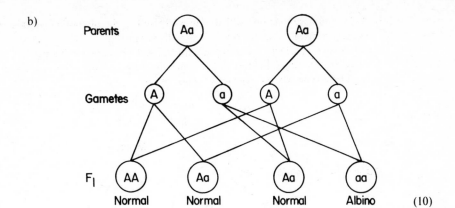

Parents: Aa — Aa

Gametes: A a A a

F₁: AA Normal, Aa Normal, Aa Normal, aa Albino (10)

c)

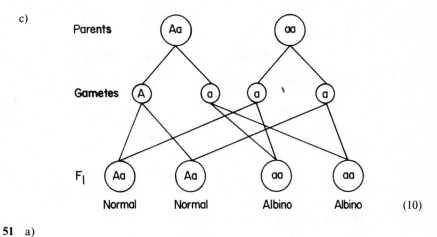

Parents: Aa — aa

Gametes: A a a a

F₁: Aa Normal, Aa Normal, aa Albino, aa Albino (10)

51 a)

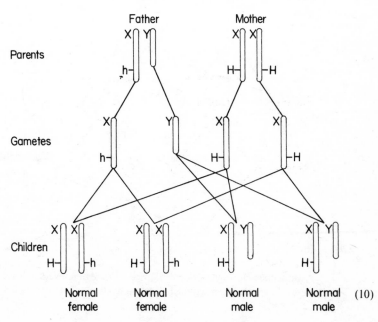

Father: X Y, h
Mother: X X, H H

Parents

Gametes: X h, Y, X H, X H

Children:
X X (H h) Normal female,
X X (H h) Normal female,
X Y (H) Normal male,
X Y (H) Normal male (10)

145

b)

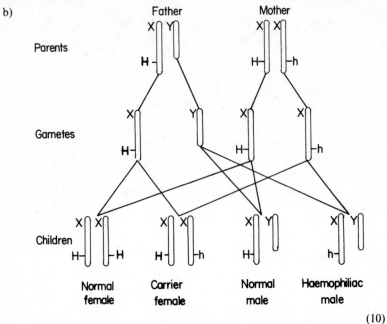

(10)

c)

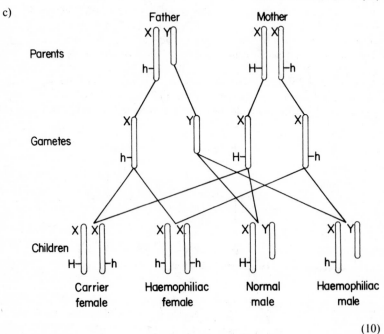

(10)

52 a) 1   Bb
     5   Bb
     7   Bb.   (3)

All must be heterozygous i.e. Bb, since all have blue-eyed children. If they were BB all children would be brown-eyed.   (2)

b) 2   bb
    3   Bb
    4   bb
    6   bb
    8   bb.   (5)
        2, 4, 6 and 8 are blue-eyed and can only have the genotype bb. 3 is
        brown-eyed—Bb. She cannot have the genotype BB since her mother
        did not carry the gene for brown eyes.
c)   9 has the genotype Bb. Her husband may be BB or Bb. If he is BB expected
        genotypic ratio is 1 BB to 1 Bb. Phenotypically all children are brown-
        eyed . If he is Bb expected genotypic ratio is 1 BB to 2 Bb to 1 bb.
        Phenotypic ratio is 3 brown-eyed to 1 blue-eyed   (10)

        (Ratios are expected ones and may vary due to small members of
        offspring)

53 a) 1   aa   4   Aa
        2   Aa   5   Aa.   (5)
        3   Aa
    b)   No. Although all children are normal and her husband has the genotype
            Aa she could have either the genotype AA or Aa. A genotype of Aa would
            be expected to produce some affected children but the fact thall all
            children are normal does not rule out this genotype. Subsequent children
            may be affected. The expected ratios are only seen with large numbers of
            offspring.   (3)
    c)   50%
    d) (i)   2 normal children with the genotype Aa, 2 affected children with the
              genotype aa.   (4)
        (ii) All affected children with the genotype aa.   (3)
        (iii) 1 normal child with the genotype AA, 2 normal children with the
              genotype Aa, 1 affected child with the genotype aa.   (4)

54 a)

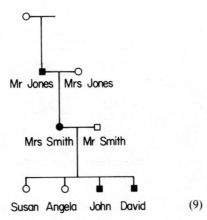

b) (i)   Pp
    (ii) pp
    (iii) Pp
    (iv) Susan—pp, Angela—pp, John—Pp, David—Pp.   (7)
c)   Mr. Jones's father. He could be either PP or Pp—either genotpye would
          produce the resulting family pedigree. Without knowing his
          ancestry it is not possible to state his genotype.   (4)

147

55 a)   Death rate and infant morality rate will fall. Number of people of
        reproductive age will rise and tendency will be for population to rise. Also
        people will tend to live longer. This will also tend to increase the
        population.   (5)
   b)   Large number of deaths will reduce population for a temporary period.
        Once effects of famine are over population will return to normal.   (5)
   c)   Birth rate will fall reducing population. If the trend continues there will be
        less people of reproductive age and this will tend to reduce the
        population even more.   (5)
   d)   Amount of available food will increase. People will be better fed and
        infant mortality will fall. Birth rate will tend to increase causing a rise in the
        population.   (5)

11. Microbiology and Disease

1	B	15	E	29	A	43	D
2	D	16	D	30	C	44	A
3	C	17	C	31	D	45	E
4	C	18	C	32	B	46	A
5	E	19	A	33	A	47	D
6	A	20	C	34	A	48	E
7	B	21	B	35	C	49	B
8	D	22	E	36	B	50	B
9	E	23	A	37	B	51	C
10	E	24	C	38	E	52	C
11	E	25	A	39	B	53	A
12	A	26	C	40	D	54	A
13	C	27	B	41	A	55	D
14	D	28	B	42	C		

56 a)

YEAR	NUMBER OF CASES OF			TOTAL DEATHS
	TUBERCULOSIS	FOOD POISONING	BOTH	
1964	1300	600	1900	25
1966	1300	700	2000	27
1968	1200	700	1900	26
1970	1100	900	2000	29
1972	900	650	1550	22
1974	700	600	1300	19

(12)

   b)   Cases of these diseases must be reported to the Health Authorities.   (2)
   c)   1970.
   d)   1965.
   e)   1973–1974.
   f)   Tuberculosis shows a downward trend food poisoning does not.   (2)
   g)   Vaccination and X-ray programmes have reduced the incidence of
        tuberculosis. No such programme against food poisoning.   (3)

148

h)	No. Some mild cases may not be diagnosed as such and therefore not reported. Some mild cases of food poisoning may not be seen by a doctor.	(3)

57 a)

DESCRIPTION	DISEASE
Spread by sexual intercourse	Gonorrhea
Can be transmitted by a dog bite	Hydrophobia
Nutritional deficiency disease	Scurvy
An inherited disease	Haemophilia
A form of cancer	Leukaemia
Caused by a fungus	Ringworm
Spread by contaminated water	Cholera
Caused by a blood fluke	Bilharziasis
Transmitted by the rat flea	Bubonic plague
A lung disease	Tuberculosis
Caused by a hormonal deficiency	Diabetes

(11)

b)

TECHNIQUE OR TREATMENT	DISEASE
Food inspection	Tapeworm
Mass Chest Radiography	Tuberculosis
Strict quarantine regulations	Hydrophobia
Chlorination of water	Cholera
Daily injections of insulin	Diabetes
Prevention of mosquitoes from breeding	Malaria
Use of the Sabin vaccine	Poliomyelitis
Use of molluscicides	Bilharziasis

(or others)	(8)

c)	Chlorination of water—chlorine forms hypochlorous acid which breaks down in contact with bacteria to release an active form of oxygen which kills the bacteria.	(3)
Mass Chest Radiography—mobile X-ray units are able to visit schools, factories, isolated villages and make it possible to screen large numbers of people for signs of the disease. Early treatment is thus possible./or others.	(3)

149

58 a) 1 In contaminated food—tapeworm/food poisoning   (2)
    2 By insect bites—malaria/sleeping sickness   (2)
    3 Via mouth or nose—tuberculosis/measles   (2)
    4 Via reproductive organs—syphilis/gonorrhea   (2)
    5 By skin to skin contact—leprosy/ringworm   (2)
    6 By direct penetration—hookworm/bilharziasis.   (2)
  b)   Rise in body temperature
        Increase in activity of white cells
        Production of antibodies/increase in heart rate.   (3)
  c)   Yes—many moulds are now known to produce antibiotics.   (2)

59 a)

	1900	1910	1920	1930	1940	1950	1960
Total No. of Deaths	430	390	360	395	435	465	756

(7)

b)

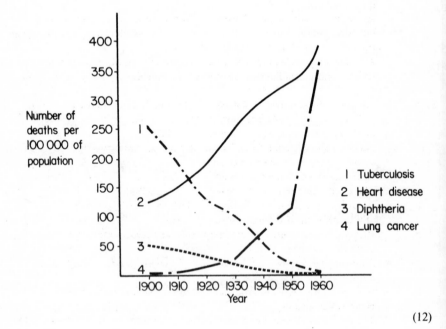

(12)

  c)   Tuberculosis and diptheria—use of vaccines and radiography.   (4)
  d)   Increased stress of modern living, increase in smoking and high fat
        consumption and lack of exercise.   (4)
  e)   BCG vaccination and mass chest X-ray.   (2)
  f)   840 deaths per 100,000 of the population.

60 a) Antiseptic methods are the means by which aseptic conditions are reached. An antiseptic is a chemical which inhibits the growth of micro-organisms.

Asepsis is the absence of pathogenic micro-organisms and may be achieved by the use of antiseptic methods or specific antiseptics. (4)

b) Active immunity provides long term protection from a disease. It is characterised by the body producing antibodies to a pathogen.

May be acquired by

  (i) inoculation of a vaccine of attenuated disease—causing organisms
  (i) by inoculation of a dead culture of the pathogen
  (iii) by inoculation of modified toxins.

Passive immunity is relatively short-lived. Given by injection of a serum containing antibodies, usually obtained from an animal which has been given a mild form the disease. It may also be acquired by passage of maternal antibodies across the placenta to the foetus. (4)

c) Infectious diseases are ones which can be transmitted from person to person. Tranmission may be by a variety of methods.

Contagious diseases can only be transmitted by direct contact with an infected person or with an article such as clothing which carries the infective agent. (4)

d) An antibiotic is a substance produced by fungi and some bacteria which kill or inhibit the growth of other bacteria. They are harmless to man and can therefore be used to treat certain diseases.

An antibody is a chemical substance produced in the blood and tissues which counteracts harmful substances produced by pathogens. (4)

61 a) An animal that carries a pathogen from one host to another. (2)

b) A chemical produced by bacteria and fungi that kills or inhibits the growth of certain species of bacteria. (2)

c) An inoculum prepared from dead or attenuated pathogens that stimulates the body to produce antibodies. (2)

d) A disease-causing micro-organism. (2)

e) The study of the cause of disease. (2)

f) Liquid derived from coagulating blood which is used to provide antitoxins against certain diseases. (2)

g) Preventative measures taken to reduce the chances of catching a particular disease. (2)

h) A large increase in the number of cases of a particular disease above the normal level in the population. (2)

i) A disease which must be reported by doctors and medical staff to the Health Authorities. (2)

j) The spread of an epidemic disease from one country to several other countries or continents. (2)

62 a) Provide optimum temperature for bacterial growth.

b) Dissolve 0.005g resazurin in 100cm^3 water. (2)

c) Sterilised—no change from original colour. (2)

d) Fresh untreated—pink colour indicates some bacteria present. (2)

e) Sour milk—white colour indicates large numbers of bacteria present. (2)

f) Boiling kills any bacteria present. (2)

g) As control—to demonstrate that bacteria-free milk remains blue. (2)

12. Social Hygiene

1	C	13	A	25	D	37	E
2	D	14	D	26	B	38	A
3	C	15	A	27	A	39	B
4	C	16	C	28	A	40	D
5	E	17	E	29	E	41	C
6	D	18	E	30	C	42	D
7	E	19	E	31	A	43	C
8	D	20	C	32	B	44	C
9	D	21	C	33	E	45	E
10	A	22	C	34	C	46	E
11	E	23	E	35	A		
12	B	24	C	36	B		

47 a) A layer of impermeable material incorporated into the walls of buildings above ground level to prevent moisture rising up the walls. (2)

b) Reduce noise, condensation and cut down heat loss and thus reduce fuel bills. (2)

c) Areas in which it is illegal to burn a smoke-producing fuel. (2)

d) A deep well, the water from which comes to the surface under pressure and is reasonably germ-free. (2)

e) Chlorine is added to water after filtration to kill any remaining bacteria. (2)

f) Methods of preservation which do not kill bacteria but arrest their growth eg. freezing. (2)

g) An international organisation which co-ordinates research into diseases, sponsors medical programmes, collects health statistics and assists in health education. (2)

h) Provides a clean source of heat which is easily controllable and can be regulated to particular circumstances. (2)

i) Cans in which the ends bulge outwards indicating a positive pressure inside caused by the respiration of anaerobic micro-organisms which will have decayed the food. (2)

j) The addition of a controlled quantity of fluoride to water supplies to help lower the incidence of dental caries. (2)

48 a) (i) Enable large numbers of people to be screened for early signs of disease (2)

(ii) Enable expectant mother to have regular medical examinations and to receive advice on hygiene and diet (2)

(iii) Provide information, advice and help regarding contraception and the dangers of unplanned pregnancy (2)

(iv) Provide a source of vitamin C (2)

(v) Reduce the chance of accidents caused by spillage of hot liquids or use of sharp utensils.   (2)

b) (i) Reservoirs of plague, food poisoning and can also transmit several other diseases to man   (2)

(ii) Deposit bacteria on food and utensils and thus spread infection   (2)

(iii) Child may mistake medicines for sweets and may be poisoned   (2)

(iv) Child may mistake poison for a drink   (2)

(v) Increased chance of catching diseases spread by droplet infection eg. tuberculosis.   (2)

49

ITEM	OPTION
International travel	Quarantine regulations
Cavity walls	Insulation
Smokeless zones	Air pollution
Water treatment	Filter beds
Sir Ronald Ross	Malaria
Joseph Lister	Antiseptic
Mongolism	Inherited disease
Asbestosis	Occupational disease
Sewage disposal	Activated sludge
Food hygiene	Refrigeration
Tuberculosis	Chest X-ray
Streptomycin	Antibiotic
Cholera epidemic	Earthquakes
Cancer of the womb	Cervical smears
Food preservation	Canning

(15)

50 a)   Pathogenic micro-organisms—disease/allow named examples
Industrial waste—poisoning
Heavy metals—lead poisoning (Allow others)   (6)

b)   Grid—settlement tank—filter bed—chlorination unit—pump house—storage tank—mains supply.   (7)

(i) Allows large particles of debris to settle out of the water

(ii) Large storage tanks on high ground where water is stored before use by consumers

(iii) Used to pump water from treatment plant to storage tank

(iv) Adds chlorine to water killing bacteria

(v) Takes water from storage tank to consumer

(vi) Filters small particles and most bacteria from water

(vii) Removes large particles of waste from water e.g. rags, twigs.   (7)

51 a)   1   Screens/Grid
2   Settling chamber
3   Trickling filter.   (3)

b)   1   Removes large particles of debris such as rags and bottles from incoming sewage

2   Allows solid matter to settle out of the sewage.   (4)

c) Effluent is pumped through a perforated pipe and trickles through a bed of coke or stones. Protozoa and bacteria act as a biological filter and the resulting liquid can be discharged into a river. (4)

d) Micro-organisms digest organic matter in sewage. (2)

e) As fertiliser, used to produce methane gas. (2)

52 a) Clean clothing must be worn
Caps must be worn
Clean gloves must be worn when handling food
No smoking
Wounds must be covered/toilet facilities must be adequate/allow others (5)

b) To prevent contamination of food.

c) Food may have to be transported long distances to the consumer. Much food is seasonal and must be preserved to enable its use to be spread over a longer period of time. (2)

d) (i) Canning—freeze drying (2)
(ii) Freezing—dehydration (2)
(iii) Sterilization—dehydration (2)
(iv) Dehydration—canning. (2)

e) Dehydration—removing water from food stops the action of natural enzymes and prevents growth of micro-organisms.
Freezing arrests the activity of enzymes and micro-organisms.
Canning—food is placed in a sealed can which prevents entry of micro-organisms, The can is heated sufficiently to destroy any micro-organisms or spores present in the food (4)

53 a) Silicosis (pneumoconiosis)—coalmining/stone—quarrying
Asbestosis—mining/asbestos processing industries
Anthrax—leather industry
Mercury poisoning—mining/industries using mercury. (Allow others) (8)

b) Silicosis, Asbestosis—use of masks to prevent inhalation, use of exhaust fans, protective clothing, clean working conditions, adequate standards of humidity and ventilation. Regular inspection of place of work and machinery. (Allow others) (7)